The

POTATO

WORLD

The
POTATO
WORLD

through illustrated varieties

by John Webster

First published in 1997 by John Webster

ISBN 0 9531461 0 3

The History of the Potato © John Webster 1997

Printed by David Winter & Son Ltd, Dundee

CONTENTS

ACKNOWLEDGEMENTS

All the potato illustrations were attributed to

Caithness Potatoes, Scotland

Angus Fertilizers, Tayside

Potato Marketing Board

The National Museums of Scotland

Angus Museums, Tayside

Grampian Growers, Montrose

Charles Maisey, Pontyclun

Claude Peace, South Ronaldsay

D.C. Thomson, Dundee

Reekie Engineering, Forfar

Websters Potatoes, Scotland

Department of Agriculture, East Craigs, Edinburgh

D. Fawcett, Kirriemuir, Angus

The Retreat, Glenesk, Tayside

FOREWARD

Potatoes provide one of the main sources of food in the Western World. There are over 200 varieties available to the housewife in reds, whites and part-coloured varieties with firm waxy, floury and soft moist textured flesh. One of the worlds finest foods, potatoes can be cooked to suit a wide range of dishes. At the turn of the century the yields were much lower than modern varieties, producing only 8 to 10 tonnes per acre with new varieties of today and the use of modern methods. The tonnage per acre is from 25 to 30 tonnes plus. This book provides the gardener, the exhibitor, the amateur and the professional grower with a wide range of information and is an invaluable guide to the Potato World.

John Webster
1997

INTRODUCTION

The largest percentage of the world's potatoes are grown in America and Europe but the range of varieties is much less in America than in Europe. One would be wrong to think of the potato as entirely western food. China is second in the world league table of producing countries, with India in fourth place. In the same way that rice has become incorporated into western diets, the potato has moved around the world and is now grown in over 80 countries world wide being second only to maize in tonnage. The potato lies fourth behind maize, rice and wheat. No other major food is so adaptable and efficient, producing a nutritious product in such a short growing season. The British consume over 200lbs of potatoes per head of population each year but the Irish and other European countries have totals of 250lbs per head of population. Potatoes are the most popular vegetable in Britain and is a major source of vitamin C. In a normal season, British farmers produce over 6½ million tonnes of potatoes per year in a wet growing season and with irrigation the tonnage can increase to well over 7½ million tonnes. Potatoes are consumed in various ways. A large percentage is sold in processed form such as canned potatoes, frozen chips and crisps being the most popular closely followed by instant mashed potato. The traditional chip is loosing its share of the market to convenience foods. Superstores have an ever increasing share of the potato market at the expense of the greengrocer. The farm gate is becoming an important point of sale with farmers selling their potatoes at keen prices by direct sales to the consumer. Since the fatal blight crisis of 1846, western Europe has seldom been short of potatoes, especially Britain. But Eastern Europe has suffered shortages from time to time. Potatoes provided Europe with vital food supplies in two world wars, potatoes being one of the main sources of food. 1992 - 93 and 1996 - 97 were bleak years for potato growers due to high yields resulting in low prices and poor demand, being the leanest years of the century for the potato trade. In recent years some supermarkets have encouraged growers to reintroduce old potato varieties back on to the market but this has proved unsuccessful as old and named varieties is of little importance to the modern housewife of today. Craigs Alliance reintroduced in 1990, Doon Star 1988, Di Vernon 1992 have all been dropped from the market after just a few years due to lack of demand. There is a greater choice of varieties on the market today than at any one time this century.

Chapter I

Growing Potatoes

THE ORIGINAL WAY

Choose a sunny south facing site away from trees, hedges and walls, with the absence of low lying pockets which may induce frosts. Potatoes for exhibition should be grown in sandy loam soils, enriched with plenty of organic matter for water retention and feeding. Add lots of peat or leaf mould (or both).

Avoid heavy clay and stoney soils as this can cause misshapen tubers. Soil should be dug late autumn or early winter if possible, and exposed to winter frosts. Plenty of compost should be added at this time. In early spring (late February - early March) depending on weather conditions, broadcast a balanced potato fertiliser at the rate of 3 to 4 ozs. per square yard, then the soil should be forked

Consignment of seed potatoes shipped to the department of Agriculture, Nairobi, Mombasa, 1930's

over or rotavated not too deeply and left for 10 to 14 days before planting, then firmed and raked level. Six inch U shaped drills are dug and a two to three inch layer of farmyard manure spread along the bottom of the drill with a further 2 ozs. of potato fertiliser sprinkled along each yard length of drill. Of course planting times depend on your show dates: March, early April for early August shows, and late April and as late as early May for late August/September shows as over matured skins do not clean to show standards.

Plantings should be carried out in stages to suit your show dates. If space allows, drills are spaced out wider for show potatoes, from 30" to 32" apart and tubers set 15" apart (in the drills). This will let air circulate around the plants making stronger plants. One will find that the plant at the end of the drill is always the strongest and produces the best tubers, so give your plants plenty of space. When the young plants are approximately 3" in height the soil between the drills should be forked over into a fine tilth, then earthing up should commence using a draw hoe. For exhibition potatoes, this is best done in stages as the plants grow on but should be finalised before the plants become too tall, to avoid damage to foliage. Plants should be kept moist at all times; never let them dry out, as this will prove disastrous, but also make sure you do not water-log the soil.

A mulch can be used between the drills to keep plants and tubers moist. Slug pellets should be spread around the plants from tuber formation onwards, as slugs can seriously damage a potato crop and ruin your whole show programme. Blight is a very serious disease for the potato crop, especially if high temperatures and high humidity coincide. Routine spraying at 10 day intervals with a reliable blight fungicide is recommended. It is not the purpose of this book to recommend a particular brand, but a good fungicide will be found in all specialist garden stores or catalogues. Any unhealthy looking plant found in your show patch should be dug out and burned, and that part of the soil disinfected using a good garden disinfectant. Remember to keep your potato plot weed free throughout the growing season.

THE MODERN WAY

This method starts off partly the same as the original way. One must choose a south facing sunny site well clear of trees, hedges and high walls, with the absence of low lying pockets which may induce late spring frosts. A light to medium soil is best for growing show potatoes, enriched with plenty of organic matter for water retention. Avoid heavy clay and stony soils. Ground should be dug late Autumn or early Winter and exposed to Winter frosts; never dig in very wet, water-logged conditions, rather delay. Ground should be forked over or rotavated in early Spring then raked level and firmed. Planting should commence early March and continue until early May as a range of plantings should be carried out if one intends to cover the early August - late September shows. This will provide a supply of fresh, smooth skinned tubers all through the show season. Planting all your potatoes early will provide over-mature rough skinned tubers by your late show dates.

Seven inch wide (approximately spade width) and six inch deep U shaped drills are dug. Spread a 3″ layer of farmyard manure or compost along the bottom of the drill, then a covering of peat, enough to cover the manure. Sprinkle 3 ozs. of potato fertiliser along each yard length of drill. Then the tubers are firmly set in the centre of the drill with rose end upward facing. Tubers are spaced 15″ apart in the drills and covered with riddled or sieved soil or peat compost and slightly ridged. Continue to earth up with sieved soil. Once enough soil-compost has been added, a mulch of straw spread between the drills will keep the crop moist. Slug pellets should be applied as the young tubers start to form.

For this method of potato growing, drills are spaced out 36″ apart. Two stakes are positioned at each end of the drill at approximately 9″ apart and 30″ to 36″ in height with further pairs of stakes (one at each side of the drill) spaced 4 ft. apart. Lines of thin wire or strong nylon string are placed the full length of drill, one at each side, and attached to each stake. 2″ x 2″ stakes are recommended for the ends of the drill, and 1″ x 1″ stakes for the centres. Wires or strings should be placed 9″ apart, the first line being positioned when the plants are approx. 8-9″ in height. This method will keep the haulms in an upright position and will let the air circulate around the plants, making stronger individual plants.

Much more space is required and more work is involved, but less potatoes need to be grown, as by this method, with tubers not coming into contact with stones and rough soil, more Show specimens will be produced from this crop than an ordinary garden crop.

IN GROW BAGS

Growing potatoes for exhibition in polythene bags is becoming very popular, and even with no garden one can grow potatoes for exhibition. Used farm fertiliser or seed grain and garden peat bags make ideal grow bags for a potato crop. Household refuse bags are rather frail. Bags are rolled approximately half way down, compost is then added and firmed to a level of 8″ from the top of the half bag, leaving space for 4″ of good sieved fertile soil or compost and 2 ozs. of potato fertiliser to be added. Check that the soil does not contain a high lime content, as lime can burn the tuber skins and encourage scab. The finished compost/soil level is 3″-4″ below the top of the bag. The compost may settle down a little so the bags are best filled at least two weeks prior to planting and topped up if required. Two bold, approximately 3 oz. sprouted tubers are planted per bag. Sprouts should not be more than 2″ long and covered by not more than 2″ of soil. The soil level can be topped up by adding additional compost later in the season if required. There is no advantage in having sprouts 3″ to 5″ long, they should be short and sturdy. Tubers should be confined to 3 strong sprouts each. Surplus sprouts should be removed prior to planting. Regular watering is essential; never let plants dry out, but don't overwater as water - logged conditions can be disastrous for a potato crop. Remember to make a few knife-slits in each bag for drainage.

Regular feeds of a balanced liquid potato fertiliser are essential for good results but over-feeding can result in oversized tubers and growth cracks.

To keep the haulms upright and to prevent them from flopping over and snapping, two canes are inserted at either side encircled with broad twine. Canes should be inserted early in the season when foliage is about 5" in height and placed well clear of the plants to avoid the young tubers coming into contact with the canes as tubers pressing against them can cause mis-shapes. Grow bags should be placed in a sheltered south facing position. It is important to name your potatoes at planting time. Plants should be protected with routine spraying at 10 day intervals with a reliable blight fungicide.

To harvest a grow bag crop the bag should be slit and opened up, the plant lifted by hand and gently shaken to release the tubers. Care should be taken not to damage them.

Grow bags can also be filled with compost not too firmly packed leaving space for the tubers to develop. The bag is sealed at the top and placed flat on the surface on this occasion. The compost mixture used is 7 parts sieved loam, 3 parts of granulated peat and 2 parts of coarse sand (all parts by loose bulk). To each bushel of this mixture, add 2 oz. of potato fertiliser.

For a soil-less compost 9 parts of granulated peat and three parts of coarse sand, both parts by loose bulk; to each bushel of this mixture add 2 oz. of potato fertiliser. Both mixtures should be thoroughly mixed. Additional feeds can be applied during the growing season such as liquid manures or foliar feeds. Three 4" x 4" insertions are made in the grow bag equally apart; then 3 sprouted tubers are planted 4" deep into the compost. A few slits should be made in the bag for drainage. Tomato grow bags are unsuitable for growing a potato crop as they are too slim and shallow and too tightly packed leaving very limited space for the tubers to swell.

RECOMMENDED SHOW VARIETIES FOR GROW BAG CULTIVATION

Baillie	Estima	Pentland Javelin	Swift
Balmoral	Home Guard	Pentland Lustre	Ulster Ensign
Cultra	Kestrel	Provost	Ulster Prince
Catriona	King Edward	Red King Edward	Valor
Diana	Morag	Shula	Vanessa
Di Vernon	Pentland Dell	Stroma	Winston

GROWING POTATOES FOR THE KITCHEN

Choose a sunny site and avoid planting under trees, near hedges or shaded by north facing walls.

The crop requires a good rich soil, well dug in late autumn or early winter. It is beneficial to have the ground dug and left rough prior to frosts as this will help to break down the soil in the spring, but never dig in very wet conditions (rather delay) as digging can be done in early spring, but I prefer late autumn-early winter digging if possible. Plenty of farmyard manure or compost should be incorporated at digging time if available. In addition compound potato fertiliser should be forked in at approximately 4 oz. per square yard prior to planting. If farmyard manure or compost has not been incorporated at digging time it can still be incorporated by spreading it along the bottom of the drill at planting time by making the drills a little deeper. Tubers can be planted directly on top of the manure. Some gardeners prefer this method rather than incorporating farmyard manure at digging time. Planting can start in very sheltered places in late February or early March for early crops.

In open sites, plant earlies from mid-March to early April, and maincrop varieties from early April to early May, earlier in the south, later in the north. Delay planting rather than plant in cold, wet or water-logged conditions. 5″ U shaped drills are dug, then 2 ozs. of a balanced potato fertiliser sprinkled along each yard length of drill. Early varieties should be given 24″ to 26″ between

Potato planting, Tayside 1950's

drills and tubers planted 14" apart in the drills. Maincrop varieties being stronger in the haulm require 28" to 30" between the drills and the tubers 15" apart in the drills. To obtain good sized tubers remove surplus sprouts leaving 3 to 4 per tuber. Once the young plants reach 3" in height the soil between the drills should be forked over to make a fine tilth for earthing up into ridges.

When the foliage reaches a height of approximately 8" a blight spray should be applied at fortnightly intervals. Early varieties for winter storage should not be harvested until fully matured. When all flowers have dropped off cut the foliage off at almost ground level and leave the crop for about 10 to 14 days before harvesting. This will give the tubers time to mature. Store potatoes for winter use in hessian sacks (not polythene) or in wooden boxes and store in a dark frost proof shed. Potatoes can also be stored in clamps (pits) made by heaping the tubers up then covering them with a thick layer of straw and a 6" layer of soil, with up to a 10" layer of soil in Northern areas where severe frosts are common. (Clamps are made in the open garden). Tubers should be covered and stored soon after digging as potato tubers green very quickly. Potatoes for over-winter storing should not be dug in wet or water logged conditions, rather delay until the soil is reasonably dry. Dispose of all cut haulms without delay – don't keep them lying around and keep them out of the compost heap.

It is common for soil to become potato sick due to close rotation. A crop rotation of 3 years is recommended if space allows, or the soil sterilised.

GROWING POTATOES IN CONTAINERS

Growing potatoes in containers, especially pots and barrels, is not new, but the introduction of plastic and polythene modules has widened the scope and interest and simplified the work involved compared with cultivating potatoes in the garden. In addition there is less slug or wireworm damage to tubers. Even with no garden or lack of space, potatoes can be grown and produced very early in the season by this method as plants can be protected from late frosts, also very late crops can be produced to give new potato flavour late in the season.

Factory-made PVC panels which interlock to form a circular bin are now very popular and available from garden centres and horticultural stockists. They are functional and hygienic and vary in sizes and diameter with 8 to 12 panels forming a convenient cylinder approximately 20" to 30" high and 24" wide. A central separate, perforated irrigation pipe 2/3" diameter sealed at the bottom will help to produce good yields. Of course container grown crops will yield less than potatoes grown in a fertile garden.

Choose a sheltered sunny site which is easily accessible and level. When erecting, the bottom of the container is crocked with about 4" of stone or rubble, then 10" of rough soil or compost and a 4" layer of well rotted farmyard manure or compost (this depends on the depth of the container) to encourage and provide for early root feeding. Spread on 4 ozs. of potato fertiliser with a further 3" to 4" of an ideal growing medium, such as John Innes No 3 or an enriched

Wire bottom gathering box top, and wicker gathering basket.

rose end facing upwards and covered with not more than 2″ of compost, adding compost as the plants grow to avoid greening the young tubers.

On cold evenings, and until all danger of frosts is past the young shoots should be covered at nights with polythene or jute sacks which are removed in the daytime. Keep the coverings away from the young shoots to avoid damage as the shoots are very tender at this stage.

Plants grow rapidly in sheltered sunny conditions during April and May, so close attention should be given to obtain best results.

Watering is a vital factor for ensuring success and plants in a container need much more than one would believe, so be generous each morning when growth is fully active, with at least one gallon of water irrespective of rain. In very hot weather watering may be required two to three times per day; never let the plants flag or droop or get waterlogged as this can prove disastrous to the project. If you feel that the plants need a booster then a foliar feed is recommended. When the foliage begins to appear above the top of the container, three or four canes or stakes should be inserted down the side and the potato stems loosely encircled with broad twine (the brittle haulms are easily snapped over by gusts of wind at this vulnerable period). This helps to hold the plants steady. By early May in the south, late May in the north, the container will have been topped up frequently with compost, plus food, as potatoes are gross feeders, so this will encourage the formation of tubers.

mixture of loam/peat and sand. Recommended tuber size is 3-4 ozs. for container planting. Tubers should be well sprouted (strong, sturdy sprouts are best). Avoid long thin sprouts. Select a vigorous reliable variety. Four tubers can be planted equally round the container approximately 5″ from the sides depending on the size of the module. Tubers should be pressed into the compost

The appearance of flower buds indicate that small potatoes are developing underneath the plant. By the end of May to the end of June depending on your part of the country. Your container crop will be ready to harvest. This is done simply by extracting one or two panels by pulling them straight upwards and folding back the remainder. Potatoes can then be picked from the plants, as the compost, now unsupported, collapses. The potato container can now be dismantled, cleaned and stored away for re-use next season, or one can grow a Christmas potato crop by some advanced planning. When normal outdoor planting of maincrops is completed in late May it is quite feasible to retain a number of tubers of a late variety and rub off all the first sprouts; these seeds should be set outside and will gradually produce fresh sprouts. By July when the container is cleared of its first crop, refill as before and plant the retained seed. Growth in the last four months of the year is much slower due to the shorter daylight and the sun's weaker heat rays, but by then good sized tubers will have been formed. These need protection against frosts by putting straw, hessian sacks or covers round the container until your Christmas harvest is ready. This is not so successful in Scotland with the severe frosts in November and December. The water rate must be cut back drastically in the later months of the season.

Potatoes grown in containers are almost free from blemishes. Scab and slugs are rare. By harvesting early in the season blight presents no problem, the tubers emerge clean and almost ready for the pot, only a wash is required. Irregular, insufficient or over

Training plots for inspectors, East Craigs, Edinburgh 1992

watering may cause growth cracks or irregular shaped tubers, but you will get a real new potato taste.

Not all varieties are suited to restricted container environment, but many of the strong growing varieties develop favourably. The earlies recommended are Duke of York, Red Duke of York, Rocket, Maris Bard, Arran Pilot, Foremost, Arran Comet, Ulster Sceptre, Kestrel, Swift, Winston, Marfona, Balmoral, Nadine, Arkula, Epicure, Estima, Dunluce, Stroma, Concurrent and Penta. The late varieties for Christmas use are Valor, Navan, Cultra, Sante, Maris Piper, Ailsa and Morag.

ORGANICALLY GROWN POTATOES

Organic potatoes are becoming more widely grown as they are produced without the use of artificial fertilisers and pesticides. However to grow a 100 per cent organic crop all materials used must be purely organic, such as farmyard manures which must come from an organic farm. All composts must be made from true organic plant materials; fertilisers must also be fully organic. There are very few organic fertilisers that are beneficial to the potato crop. The most useful are bone meal and bone flour, preferably bone flour as it is quicker acting. Applied at the rate of 4 ozs. per square yard, it should be applied prior to planting. Blood, fish and bone are also useful; the blood acts first then the fish with the bone meal later, but don't use both. If the blood, fish and bone is used it should be applied at the rate of 2 ozs. per yard length of the drill at planting time to produce a good potato crop.

Potash is essential and rock potash can be applied at the rate of 6 - 8 ozs broadcast per square yard. Farmyard manure is beneficial to the potato crop and was widely used for potato crops long before artificial chemical fertilisers were invented and it is still widely used for garden crops today.

Farmyard manure is best spread along the bottom of the potato drill at the rate of 2" - 3" deep with the potato tubers planted directly on top and pressed into the manure with rose end facing upwards. Seaweed is also beneficial to the potato crop with its potash content. This is best gathered in the early autumn and incorporated into the soil at digging time or piled up and mixed with farmyard manure starting with one 6" layer of farmyard manure, then a 6" layer of seaweed. Continue with a layer of each until the pile is completed, then top cover with a few inches of soil and leave over winter. The material will be well rotted by planting time. Of course everyone can't obtain seaweed. However, calcified seaweed can be found in your garden shop and applied at approximately 4 oz. per square yard, broadcast and forked into the soil at least two weeks prior to planting. Well rotted compost can be used and applied at the rate of 2"-3" spread along the bottom of the drills at planting time with seed tubers planted directly on top of the compost, again pressed in with rose end facing upwards. Once the plants are approximately 5" in height foliar feeds can be applied at 10 day intervals if the crop requires a booster, but do not overfeed your potatoes.

Seaweed extracts, which supply essential trace elements and promote natural growth, are an ideal foliar feed. Seaweed liquid fertilisers can also be watered into the soil to boost the crop. Garden lime must be avoided as it will cause common scab. Blight is a very serious disease in potato crops and when growing organic the choice of blight sprays is very limited indeed. Bordeaux mixture (a traditional fungicide) can be used as a preventative spray against potato blight. Another remedy is to cut off the haulms at almost ground level provided that the tubers are of usable size, but this must be carried out at the very first signs of the disease as blight can travel through the plant system very quickly. All cut haulms should be removed from the garden immediately and burned where possible. Tubers saved from a blight attack should not be used for seed.

When growing organic potatoes it is an advantage to select varieties that have some resistance to blight disease. Slugs can cause serious damage to the potato crop by boring holes in the tubers. As pellets cannot be applied to an organic crop the alternative is Fertosan Slug killer which is a preparation

harmless to birds, hedgehogs, pets, earthworms and soil micro-organisms. It is not a bait but acts as a contact agent causing shrinkage to the slime producing organs of slugs and snails; in olden days agricultural salt was used as a slug killer, by applying the salt in the bottom of the drill (between rows) and kept well away from the plants. Salt is very effective against slugs and snails. The most common slug to attack potato tubers, the keel slug, which appears in late evening/early morning to feed. Varieties with some resistance to slug damage, such as firm textured varieties are recommended for organic growing.

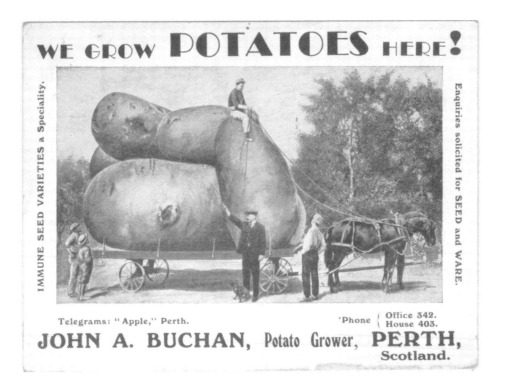

Advertising postcard for John A. Buchan, Perth

HARVESTING AND CLEANING SHOW POTATOES

When flowers have dropped off the plants, the tubers should be almost the size for exhibiting, with the dates of your flower shows noted. At this stage the haulms should be cut off, almost at ground level, at least 10 to 14 days prior to being dug, this will allow the tuber skins to firm and be less easily damaged. It is best to dig the tubers for exhibition on a cool dry evening, avoiding hot sun or rain. Rainy weather often means that tuber tentacles or pores are wide open and this can lead to unattractive skins with black-grey spots appearing when dried.

Some varieties are more prone to this than others. A broad fork is best for digging show potatoes. Insert the fork well below each plant – the soil roots and tubers are then gently eased up and out of the drill. Do not shake the plant with the fork, but use a little shake by the hand to find the tubers. When sufficient tubers are selected put them into a plastic bucket in cold water, leaving them in the water for 45 minutes, to loosen any soil that may stick to the tubers, then wash them under a cold water tap (do not use hot water). Apply a spot of washing-up liquid into the sponge occasionally and check the eyes for soil particles, using a very soft brush gently applied under water – short fingernails are essential to avoid scratches. Once the tubers are cleaned set them on a towel to dry off. Cover with another towel to keep them from greening and leave them drying for at least an hour or more.

Prior to packing, the tubers are rolled in soft tissue paper, packed into a box in separate layers and named. Show potatoes can be dug, prepared and packed, up to a week prior to a show. Always get them ready in good time – never do a rushed job. When showing a number of varieties, one variety dug, selected, washed and packed is enough for one evening. Do not set your exhibits out on the show bench too early – one hour prior to judging time is sufficient but of course one can have other commitments and cannot stage exhibits at the most suitable time. Always select a few spare tubers and take them to the show as a stand-by in case of damage.

Potatoes are staged on white paper plates with rose end outward facing. Most shows provide classes for round coloured, long coloured, round white and long white. Shows will have different amounts per plate. Potatoes can also be exhibited in a shallow box filled with sawdust. 4 varieties, 4 tubers of each is very popular in Scotland (see picture). All tubers should be named with the exception of some small shows which do not enforce naming. Always cover your exhibits with newspapers to avoid greening. The show stewards will remove the papers prior to judging time.

What The Judges Will Look For

Nicely shaped tubers of equal size, with smooth clean skins are looked for, as are shallow eyes with low eyebrows and shallow heels along with nice presentation.

Tuber Size for Showing

Medium sized tubers are best for exhibiting (from 5 to 8 oz). Other sizes can be exhibited, but I prefer good sized tubers.

Tuber Shape & Planting Size for Shows

We all like to plant nicely shaped tubers, but this makes no difference to the outcome whatsoever. New seed will be field grown, and mis-shaped tubers are caused by contact with stones. When tubers are planted in different conditions the new crop will produce good shaped tubers. The best planting size tubers for show results is from golf ball size to large egg size. Should larger tubers be planted, reduce the number of sprouts to two or three per tuber, as too many sprouts will result in a large amount of small potatoes which are useless for the show bench.

Harvesting and baging early crop in the field, Tayside late 1940's.

GROWING POTATOES IN POTS AND BUCKETS

Very early crops can be produced by growing potatoes in 10″ to 12″ pots or standard sized household buckets. Plantings can start late February and continue in succession until late March. At least two plantings can be made which will produce a supply some weeks apart. The containers should have 1″ or 2″ of crocks inserted in the bottom to provide drainage. The buckets will require a few holes pierced in the bottom for drainage. One tuber is planted per pot/bucket, bedded in 4″ to 5″ of a rich compost such as John Innes No. 3 or a similar peat based compost. Seed tubers should be pre-sprouted (short and sturdy), recommended tuber size is approximately 3 ozs. The containers can be placed under the greenhouse bench. Compost should be kept moist if the greenhouse is heated. Compost will dry out very quickly so checks should be made at least once or twice daily. Once in full growth the plants will require lots of water, but should not be over-watered.

Plants should not be kept too long in a heated greenhouse as quick growth will encourage tall spindly plants. Remove the plants to a cool greenhouse or a sheltered sunny position in the garden. Plants must be protected at nights from late frosts. A cold frame open during daytime and partly closed at nights is recommended if available. The alternative is a polythene cover or tent. Additional liquid or foliar feeds with a high potash content is beneficial to the crop. To prevent the stems from flopping over and snapping two canes should be inserted at either side of the pot or bucket, encircled with broad twine. When the plants are nearing maturity the crop is sampled by simply tipping over the most mature plant and picking off the tubers. The skins at this stage will be very tender and will wash off easily, ready for the pot.

This will start off your new season potatoes. Most early varieties will flourish in this size and type of container. Blight should not be a problem as the crop will be harvested well before blight attacks.

GROWING POTATOES UNDER POLYTHENE

Potatoes are becoming widely grown under black polythene for early cropping. Good results can be obtained by this method, both for exhibition and garden use. A 4 ft. wide semi-raised bed is ideal for this type of growing. The drills are spaced at 28″ apart (in the centre of bed) leaving a 10″ space at either side. 4″ x 4″ insertions are cut out of the polythene and the tubers are planted 14″ apart (measurements taken from centre of the insertions). 4 ft. beds can be contained with at least a 2 ft. space left between each bed for tending to the crop.

The polythene is pegged down at each side of the bed with pegs (or sealed with soil) to keep it in place. Two even-flow plastic irrigation tubes are placed under the polythene, spaced apart in the centre of each bed. The plants must be kept moist, and additional watering can be applied with a watering can to plants individually. The soil should be forked over to a fine tilth, with plenty of compost or well rotted farmyard manure incorporated some weeks prior to planting, and 4 ozs. of potato fertiliser per square yard worked into the top 3" at least one week before planting. Pre-sprouted tubers (approximately one inch sprouts, retaining the 3 strongest) are planted with the top of the tuber about 4" below the polythene. A few slug pellets should be spread around each plant commencing mid season and continued at 10 day intervals for exhibition potatoes. The top 4" - 5" of the bed can be made up of Soil-less Compost mixture with added potato fertiliser at the rate of 4 oz. per square yard. Additional high potash liquid or foliar feeds are beneficial to the crop in the growing season. A blight spray is essential at 10 day intervals to prevent blight attack.

VARIETIES RECOMMENDED FOR EXHIBITION

Part-coloured Varieties

Ambo	Di Vernon	Penta
Angus Beauty	Drayton	Pentland Beauty
Balmoral	Figaro	Pentland Lustre
Brodick	Gladstone	Picasso
Cara	Glamis	Shula
Carama	Kestrel	Ulster Ensign
Catriona	King Edward	Ulster Premier
Craigs Royal	Mein's Early Round	Ulster Classic
Cultra	Merline	Verena

Coloured Varieties

Alhamra	Heather	Red Pentland Lustre
Antar	Kenzy	Red Ulster Premier
Barna	Maxine	Romano
Blush	Pollocks Pink	Rooster
Bonnie Dundee	Red Cara	Stemster
Cleopatra	Red Craigs Royal	Stroma
Diana	Red Drayton	Symphona
Fanfare	Red King Edward	Tristar
Gracia	Red Pentland Beauty	Vanessa

White Varieties

Arran Comrade	Home Guard	Sante
Avalanche	Monalisa	Sherine
Baillie	Morag	Stamina
Bishop	Nadine	Swift
Concurrent	Pentland Dell	Ulster Prince
Croft	Pentland Ivory	Ulster Sceptre
Dr McIntosh	Pentland Javelin	Vandika
Estima	Provost	Waregem

Chapter II

Potato Breeding and Breeders

Potato breeding has a long history. It is thought to have begun outside of South America soon after the potato was introduced into Europe at the end of the sixteenth century. For a long time it was thought that breeding consisted of raising seedlings from naturally set berries. It was not until the seventeenth century that planned pollinations were made.

The first reference to distinct varieties in Britain was in 1730. In that year the Irish writer George Rye described varieties of which one, The Black Potato, was praised very highly as a good keeper. The breeding of new varieties in Europe accelerated first by the blight epidemics of 1845 and following years and secondly after 1915 by the recognition of the importance of immunity to wart disease (Synchytrium Endobioticum). It can be argued that most potato breeding is technology rather than science. For example, it is unnecessary for a potato breeder to understand how yield is determined, how many genes are involved, and how they interact, especially as potato varieties are reproduced vegetatively. All the breeder needs to know is that high yielding seedlings can be selected from certain crosses, and it is much more important for him to be able to select the high yielding plants efficiently, than to understand the genetical basis of yield.

Much potato breeding still is, and will for many years, continue to be crossing a variety with high yield and poor quality or low dis-

ease resistance, with another variety of mediocre yield, but good quality or high disease resistance, in order to evolve a new variety which has a yield as high or higher than the first variety, but with the good quality or high disease resistance of the other variety. The above, however, does not mean that the breeder can ignore the genetics of the crop he is working with - nor that advances in the basic scientific knowledge are not important for plant breeding. Both may be important to the breeder in planning the crosses necessary to obtain the required combinations of characters, and in deciding the best methods for selecting and testing the improved varieties.

WILLIAM PATERSON
1810 - 1870

One of the earliest Scottish breeders was William Paterson of Dundee who was named the "mother" of modern potatoes. William Paterson was born on his father's farm, Seafield, Dundee in 1810. Seafield is now entirely covered by industrial buildings and residential property. Educated at Dundee Grammar School and St Andrews University, Mr Paterson commenced experimenting with potatoes when in his teens and went into business on his own account in 1833. He was the first person to cross fertilise and extract seed from plums (or apples)

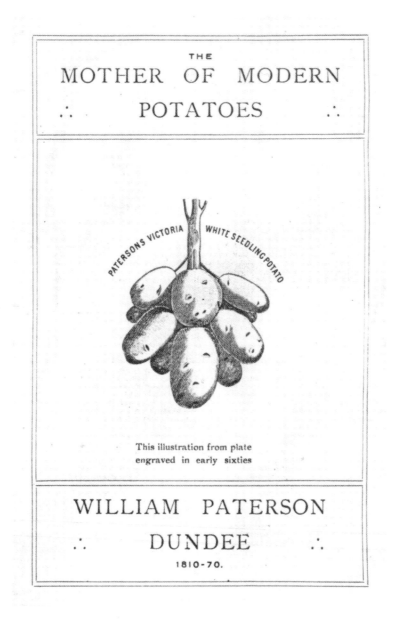

THE
MOTHER OF MODERN
∴ POTATOES ∴

PATERSONS VICTORIA WHITE SEEDLING POTATO

This illustration from plate
engraved in early sixties

WILLIAM PATERSON
∴ DUNDEE ∴
1810-70.

which at that time were little bigger than peas. His expert advice was called for during the fatal blight of 1846. During the blight he worked with government officials to enquire into the cause of the epidemic and if possible to find an antidote. He was of the opinion that there was no remedial cure, blight being caused by atmospheric action on plants, having the seeds of the disease within itself and thus it was only destined to serve its generation, the same as animal life. Without a constant and regular successive renewal from the seed of the plum or apple it would as before die out.

Paterson was the first man to make an outstanding contribution towards potato research into new varieties. He realised that the varieties he was working with in Scotland had become degenerate and lacked pure fruiting (berries) from which selection could be made. In an effort to combat this, he invested about £7,000 to import potato stocks from Central America, Chile, East and West Indies, Australia and The Cape of Good Hope and planted these promiscuously with the variety Rock, imported into Scotland from Ireland in 1848. Most of the plants produced flowers but unfortunately only a few plums and apples from which new seed were obtained. From this seed countless varieties of present day potatoes are descended. Paterson gifted and sold unnamed seedlings to leading agriculturalists of the world and put the following varieties under the name of Paterson: York Regent, White Rock, Early Red Kidney, White Kidney, Napoleon, Regent, Fluke, Alexandra, Zebra, Early Perfection, Victoria, Fluke Seedling, Princess of Lorne, Red Regent, British Queen The First, New Perthshire Red, Irish Blue, Scotch Blue, Blue Kidney, New Albert, Fortyfold, Bovinia (Cattle Feeder), Scotch Red and Blue Kidney.

Paterson did so much for Ireland during the potato famine, 1846 - 1849, that a monument was proposed in his honour. His son George who was essential to his labours was assumed a partner in 1862, but sadly he died on 1st January, 1865 at the early age of 30 years. William Paterson himself died on 3rd January, 1870, aged 60 years, bringing an end to the Paterson family. William Paterson is most remembered for his famous variety Victoria White Seedling potato (bred in 1863). Victoria produced a good yield of bold tubers and kept well in storage during the winter. Victoria achieved much success as a top quality potato. Paterson had rigorously selected the seed from one of his other varieties named Fluke; only tubers selected from the best and healthiest plants were selected and used for his breeding programme.

The most interesting claim associated with Victoria is its alleged immunity from blight: it was thought to have resistance to blight, which it did seem to have for some years. However, crops of Victoria became blight infected in the early 1870's, and growers abandoned it for other varieties. In the early days Victoria was thought to be the first blight resistant variety ever introduced. However the standard of breeding was raised, with future breeding using Victoria in the hope of emulating Paterson's successes with the variety. Many varieties bred in the late 1800's and early 1900's were bred from Victoria and still exist today.

Potato seedlings at development stage.

The following are all that are now remembered of honours won: Erfurt (Hanover) Medal and Diploma of Honour as saviour of the potato in Europe 1865. Silver Eporgne Claret Jug to descend to George from landed proprietors, farmers and friends as a token of esteem and in recognition of improving and renewing the potato plant, 1865. Oldham Medal of Manchester - Liverpool Society 1865. Specially thanked and complimented by the president of Society of Agriculture, Berlin, 1869.

Gold Medal from the Royal Highland and Agricultural Society for Experiments in Propagating New and Superior Varieties of the Potato Plant, 1869. Manchester and Liverpool Medal and Diploma in recognition of 40 Years Experiments, 1870.

ARCHIBALD FINDLAY
1841-1921

Scottish farmer Archibald Findlay, born in Auchtermuchty, Fife, Scotland, in 1841 was the most successful potato breeder of the Victorian-Edwardian era. Introducing many new varieties to the UK market, some of his most successful varieties were Majestic, Catriona, Up-To-Date, Royal Kidney and Eldorado (later renamed Evergood) and many others. Some are still with us today. Findlay held his own exhibitions of new seedlings annually, with open days at his farm in Fife, when farmers, growers and potato merchants would attend from all over the country. Demonstrations were also held at the farm in his heyday, showing cross pollination and the raising of new varieties. However, he was said to be a man who did not disclose much information on how he selected his seedlings. Visitors to his farm were given previews of the new varieties. In trials it was said that potato enthusiasts would offer amazingly high prices for new Findlay introductions. He was very much recognised for his outstanding work for the potato industry. Around the turn of the century a series of adverse summers caused a potato shortage which resulted in a potato boom early in the twentieth century, when growers sought desperately to find new and more productive varieties. Findlay, with his vast selection of new seedlings, featured prominently with very high prices being paid for his new varieties.

The variety Evergood was very much in the limelight of the potato boom in 1902. It was said that a dozen tubers of Evergood were sold for a staggering price of £160 and that £100 was offered for one single tuber of Evergood and that Findlay was offered £2,000 for the entire stocks of Evergood which was renamed Eldorado. In later years Findlay moved from his native Scotland to Langholme, Lincolnshire, where his knowledge of potato growing was very much in demand. Later still he wrote extensively for farming journals such as The Lincolnshire, and the Boston and Spalding Free Press. Findlay died in 1921.

ROBERT FENN
1816 - 1912

Fenn lived in Sulhampsted, Berkshire where most of his breeding work was carried out. He was a hobby breeder with moderate success. His most successful introduction was International Kidney, followed by other varieties such as Filbasket, Reading Abbey, Early Border, Woodstock Kidney, Prizetaker, Ringleader, Reading Ruby, Reading Russet, Early Market, Early Regent and Fiftyfold. Most of these varieties performed well in trials, but of course, there were few potato trials in Fenn's time. His introductions were mostly marketed by Suttons Seeds of Reading. International Kidney is also known as Suttons Early Regent and Jersey Royal. No certified stocks of these varieties are grown today. Ware crops of Jersey Royals are still grown in Jersey.

JAMES CLARK
1825 - 1890

Clark was a hobby breeder who operated from his home in Christchurch, Hampshire. His main occupation was the fruit and vegetable trade. Clark also had a great interest in potato breeding and introduced many new varieties to the market including Clark's Aristocratic Kidney, Reading Hero, Suttons Seedling, Clark's Cranemoor, Clark's Late Winter, Clark's White Kidney and Magnum Bonum, which can still be found in private collections and is still used by breeders today. In the search for new potato varieties the variety Epicure was the result of Clark's potato breeding and although introduced after his death it is an outstanding variety that is still in production. Epicure was the most widely grown variety in Ayrshire, Scotland, until recently, when higher yielding varieties were introduced. However Epicure is very reliable against late frosts, making a good recovery.

JOHN CLARKE
1889-1980

John Clarke of Mosside, Co. Antrim Northern Ireland was one of the best known and most successful potato breeders this century, brought up on his father's farm where he started work at an early age. Taking an active interest in the growing and development of potatoes, such was his fame world wide that students visited and other agricultural parties such as potato breeders and botanists travelled to observe and to learn his crossing skills and the selecting of potato seedlings. Clarke moved to new land due to eelworm infestation but remained in the Northern locality. Mr Clarke was awarded the O.B.E. for his work in the potato industry and on his retirement he moved South to the Dublin area. Mr Clarke introduced the well known Ulster range. His first introduction Ulster Cromlech was released in 1934 followed by Ulster Monarch (1936), Ulster Chieftain (1938), Ulster Com-merce (1939), Ulster Earl (1943), Ulster Premiere (1945), Ulster Ensign (1946), Ulster Leader (1947), Ulster Prince (1947), Ulster Emblem (1948), Ulster Supreme (1948), Ulster Dale (1950), Ulster Knight (1953), Ulster Torch (1953), Ulster Goza (1954), Ulster Beacon (1954), Ulster Malta (1955), Ulster Tarn (1956), Ulster Glen (1958), Ulster Ranger (1958), Ulster Grove (1959), Ulster Magnet (1960), Ulster Glade (1962), Ulster Sovereign (1962), Ulster Sceptre (1964), Ulster Classic (1967), Ulster Concord (1968), Ulster Viscount (1968), Ulster Lancer (1972), Ulster Brevet (1972), Ulster Chieftain, Ulster Prince and Ulster Sceptre are currently on the U.K. national list and are still in cultivation today.

CHARLES SPENCE
1878-1965

Scottish farmer Charles Spence of Tyne-field Farm, Prestonkirk, Dunbar, in the Lothians of Scotland raised and introduced the well known Dunbar varieties, named after the town of Dunbar. Spence, born in the Shetland Isles, came of an agricultural family and settled in the Lothians of Scotland at an early age where he later farmed around 300 acres of land. One of his main interests was potato breeding, raising thousands of seedlings, selecting the best and discarding thousands for different faults. His main aim was to produce varieties of quality. The only potatoes grown on his farm were the Dunbar range raised by himself. His first introduction, Dunbar Cavalier, was released in 1929 but the variety was never grown in quantity, due to low yield compared with other new varieties of the era. Dunbar Cavalier proved susceptible to virus problems. The variety was followed by further introductions bred by Spence. Dunbar Yeaman (1932), a Duke of

York cross which had a very smooth skin finish giving it show potential. However, it became unpopular with commercial growers due to yielding problems. Dunbar Archer (1936) also attempted to make a breakthrough to the commer-cial market but did not seem to catch on, more or less for the same reasons as Dunbar Yeoman. However, Mr Spence did achieve great success with further introductions. Dunbar Rover (1936) won him the Lord Derby Gold Medal in 1937. Dunbar Rover was a particularly heavy yielding variety compared with other varieties of the 1930's. The demand for second earlies, when compared to maincrop was small. Dunbar Rover was seen as a rival to Catriona British Queen and Royal Kidney. Dunbar Standard was the other high quality variety from the Spence stable which became popular very quickly all over Britain with thousands of acres grown in the late 1930's and 1940's. The variety became known for its excellent cooking qualities, and high yields. Both Dunbar Rover and Dunbar Standard are still in production today, nearly 60 years on, with virus tested and elite stocks grown in Scotland and Ireland for future production.

JOHN NICOLL
1830-1890

Scottish gardener, John Nicoll was born in Angus, Scotland, in 1830. Mr Nicoll was parks superintendent in the town of Arbroath. He served his apprenticeship on Lord Dalhousie's estate at Brechin Castle, near Brechin, Angus. Nothing in Mr Nicoll's career as a practical gardener brought him more credit than his success in the breeding and culture of potatoes. Both Paterson and Nicoll were breeding potatoes in the same era only 16 miles from each other. His most successful introduction was the variety he named Champion. At the time of its introduction many other varieties had fallen into wide-spread disease. Growers were looking for a variety with good disease resisting qualities which they found in Champion, being much more resistant to diseases than other varieties. Mr Nicoll based his potato breeding on Paterson's Victoria, raising thousands of seedlings from berries of Victoria plants. However Champion held its grip on the market in both Scotland and Ireland. A staggering 320,620 acres of Champion were planted in Ireland in 1917. Until the 1930's it was Ireland's most popular potato, and was grown commercially in Scotland until the late 1940's. Champion is no longer grown commercially but appears in private collections. Mr Nicoll spent most of his spare time breeding new potato varieties. Such was his fame, that in 1879 he was called before a House of Commons select committee at the instance of Mr Barclay, M.P. as a leading witness on the subject of potato culture. He also gave evidence as to how failures of the potato crop could be diminished. The main points of his evidence was said to be that the life of a new potato variety was only twenty to thirty years, and that Champion's superiority was not based on any unique breeding, but by selection of seedlings.

DONALD MACKELVIE
1867-1947

Donald Mackelvie was one of the foremost potato breeders in the first half of the twentieth century. The proprietor of a general merchant's business, prior to taking up potato breeding as a hobby in the early years of the century. He became a full-time breeder in later years. Introducing his first variety in 1911 which was Arran Chief, to be followed later by a full range of Arran varieties such a Arran Treasure in 1914. Although raised and named by Mackelvie he decided to withhold it from the market because of its poor cooking qualities, however, it did have many other features such as immunity from wart disease and most other diseases, and with good keeping qualities. Mackelvie, however, decided that the variety was not his usual standard and not worthy of the brand name Arran. As a result the variety was renamed Ally and marketed by other potato companies. Ally become popular in later years and large acreages were successfully grown and marketed in both England and Scotland.

Potato picking, Angus 1960's

Further Arran varieties continued to be introduced such as Arran Rose, Arran Comrade, Arran Victory and Arran Leader (1918); Arran Crest (1928); Arran Cairn (1929); Arran Peak (1930); Arran Pilot and Arran Scout (1931); Arran Signet (1934); Arran Bard (1935); Arran Viking (1945).

Arran Comet (1956) was introduced after Mackelvie's death. Arran Pilot was Mackelvie's most widely grown variety and held a good position on the U.K. market as a first early for at least 40 years and is still grown today over 50 years after its introduction. As the variety is of waxy texture it has been more widely grown in England and Wales for early cropping, being a popular variety in Cornwall and Pembrokeshire in the early years after its introduction. It is mostly grown in Scotland for seed rather than ware production.

JOHN WATSON
1902-1986

John Watson, son of an Ayrshire farmer joined McGill & Smith in 1916. He commenced plant breeding in 1921 under the guidance of J. M. McGill. He bred all the Doon varieties, such as Doon Star (1928); Doon Pearl (1921); Doon Early (1934); Doon Bounty (1939); Doon Eire (1943); Doon

Harvesting in Tayside, 1950's

Castle (1943) and Doon Well (1943). Doon Star was the most successful variety in the Doon range and is still grown in commercial production today, over sixty years on.

Other varieties bred by John Watson were Ballydoon (1931) and Home Guard (1942). He discarded Home Guard as he thought it was of no use. The variety was then developed by local farmers in Ayrshire and turned out to be a successful variety and is still grown in quantity today. Mr Watson was awarded two Lord Derby Gold medals in recognition of his work in potato breeding. All Watson's introductions were marketed by McGill & Smith, the Ayr based seed company.

POST WAR POTATO BREEDING IN SCOTLAND

Early post war potato breeding in Scotland was carried out by the Scottish Crop Research Institute formerly named the Scottish Society for Research in Plant Breeding. Formed in 1920 the original site was Craigs House, Edinburgh, but it was transferred to Pentland Field, Edinburgh in 1954. Some of the first varieties to be released from this breeding station were the Craigs Range such as Craigs Defiance (1938), Craigs Bounty (1946), Craigs Royal (1947), Craigs Snowhite (1947) and Craigs Alliance (1948), followed by the Pentland Range: Pentland Ace (1955), Pentland Beauty (1955), Pentland Crown (1959), Pentland Dell (1961), Pentland Glory (1963), Pentland Hawk (1966), Pentland Ivory (1966), Pentland Javelin (1968), Pentland Capa (1968), Pentland Lustre (1969), Pent-

land Marble (1970), Pentland Meteor (1970), Pentland Raven (1970) and Pentland Squire (1970).

Due to food shortages during the war years 1939-1945, potato crops were grown in short rotation which encouraged the build-up of potato eelworm so the main post-war potato research was focused on the breeding of eelworm resistant varieties.

Pentland Squire

HOBBY BREEDERS

In the early days of potato breeding in Britain and Continental Europe most breeding was done by hobby breeders with great success, producing some of our top introductions over the decades. Hobby breeders are still doing a good job today producing some of the most prolific varieties of the century. Although not so common in Britain nowadays, they are still very popular in Holland, where the Dutch seed export business is a model success in Europe (mainly due to the hobby breeder). The large Dutch seed companies rely heavily on the efforts of the private breeders such as amateurs for their success and they are the ones who have been responsible for many top-selling Dutch varieties in the last twenty years. Large potato companies in Britain have introduced many new Dutch varieties on to the UK markets.

Dr Jack Dunnett

One can think of only one successful British breeder left today in the private sector, and that is Scotlands Jack Dunnett of the Caithness Group. On leaving the state-controlled plant breeding station at Pentland Field to go it alone in the late 1970's, he has developed a line of crosses which have pro-

duced top varieties such as Heather (1993), Nadine (1987), Stemster (1986), Stroma (1989), Tristar (1993), Maxine (1993), Valor (1993), Winston (1992), Kestrel (1992), Argos (1995), Stamina (1992), Karama (1990), Figaro (1993) and Swift (1993). Dr Dunnett's success is not just confined to the U.K., his Scottish-bred varieties are attracting great interest abroad.

THE INTRODUCTION OF THE GOLDEN WONDER

The Golden Wonder was discovered and introduced by John Brown of Peasiehill Farm in the Arbroath district of Scotland in 1906. The Golden Wonder is a variant of the variety Langworthy, which was originally called maincrop and raised by James Clark of Christchurch in Hampshire in 1876, and renamed Langworthy in 1902 by Mr J. Niven of Perth. A very distinctive variety that is highly renowned for its excellent potato taste and quality. Dry matter is high, often in excess of 30 per cent. Few other varieties can claim that percentage – this makes it ideal for chipping and as a jacket potato. Growth is vigorous and tubers have good resistance to blight and common scab. It keeps well in over-winter storage and tubers can stay really firm to the end of May.

With these attributes Golden Wonder is easily separated from other varieties, creating a class of its own. The variety never found much success in the English markets due to its floury texture. In recent years English, French and Italian chefs have shown an interest in the Golden Wonder. After tasting and cooking trials many large hotels have placed orders for regular supplies of the variety. As much as 14,000 acres have been grown (in one year). In Scotland and Ireland from time to time adverse yields can be experienced if grown on light soils. As Golden Wonder is a gross feeder it requires plenty of farmyard manure incorporated to produce good yields. There is some confusion about the year of introduction – some records claim that the year was 1906, but the proper date was 1904. It was exhibited at Smithfield Show in London that year by John Brown. John Brown was honoured by fellow farmers from all over the County of Angus in February 1936 for his long and outstanding services to agriculture and with special congratulations for his work to the potato industry. Mr Brown was presented with a deposit receipt subscribed for by Angus Agriculturalists for his work on the introduction of the potato variety Golden Wonder.

Golden Wonder crop, 1990.

Chapter III

The Phytosanitary Advantages of Scottish Seed Potatoes

THE BASICS

The purchaser of potato seed-tubers must be able to obtain the tubers in the desired size-range, in the cultivar of choice, with high health status and in a suitable physiological condition. Potato seed tubers grown in Scotland are the products of skilled and specialist husbandry, based on the highest possible standard of pre-basic stock and shortened generation cycles, monitored by a rigorous regulatory authority and backed-up by a well-developed system of research, extension and advice to the farming community. Seed are produced of varieties (cultivars) bred within Scotland and, also, of popular varieties bred elsewhere.

The high health status of the industry is supported through advice and scientific expertise provided by the Seed Potato Inspectorate, the Scottish Agricultural Science Agency (SASA), the Scottish Agricultural College (SAC), and the Scottish Crop Research Institute (SCRI), all supported by government through the Scottish Office Agriculture, Environment and Fisheries Department. These organisations provide a complete service to the seed potato industry from basic and applied research on problems of disease, physiology, agronomy, and storage to practical advice to individual growers.

APHIDS AND VIRUS

As a result of its location on the northwest edge of Europe, Scotland enjoys (or suffers) cooler temperatures and higher wind-speeds during the potato growing season than most other European countries. These climatic characteristics allow the production of crops with very high health status for a number of important virus diseases that are spread by aphids. Most of the important aphid vectors overwinter on weeds and brassica crops are usually killed by hard frosts; mild winters would favour their survival. In Scotland's cool, northerly climate, aphid proliferation starts later and takes longer, leading to fewer generations in a season: consequently, aphid populations never reach the levels found at lower latitudes. Diseases caused by viruses, such as potato leaf-roll virus (PLRV) and potato viruses A and Y (PVA, PVY) are, therefore, much less of a problem in Scotland than in other parts of Europe. In summers that follow mild winters, however, even in Scotland, conditions can favour the potential spread of aphid-borne viruses but there are no arable crop species and very few weed species that can act as alternative hosts for aphid-borne viruses such as PLRV, PVA, and PVY. the main risk comes from the early colonisation of young crops, which are particularly susceptible to infection, because aphids can spread virus from plants growing from infected tubers before symptoms are visible and growers can identify and rogue infected plants. A network of aphid suction traps, operated by SASA, SCRI and SAC, provides information on the dates of flight and numbers of migrating aphids. Models developed form data obtained with these traps are used to assess the need for aphid control in early season and to predict the incidence of leaf-roll.

In Scotland, unlike areas in which aphids and sources of virus are numerous, the early application of systemic insecticides controls the spread of PLRV in seed potato crops. PLRV is confined to the phloem tissues of plants and systemic insecticides prevent vectors from feeding long enough to acquire the virus and they cannot then transmit it. However, viruses such as PVA and PVY can be acquired and spread by aphids making only brief probes and few insecticides kill aphids fast enough to control the spread of such viruses. (Recent surveys showed that PVY spreads very rapidly in ware crop areas of England, where aphid activity was considerably greater than it is in Scotland). Current advice in Scotland is to protect seed potato crops against all types of aphid-borne virus using insecticide mixtures combining rapid intoxicant and systemic and fumigant action: this gives excellent control. Granular aphicides are incorporated in the soil at or before planting and seed crops are sprayed routinely from about 80% emergence in response to Advisory Service warnings, with subsequent applications every 10-14 days. In addition, because aphid control on its own is no guarantee of full suppression of virus spread, and over-dependence on insecticides may select for resistant aphids, seed potato crops are regularly inspected to ensure that potential virus sources are eliminated and to identify crops at risk if aphids are detected.

Until recently, virus detection in the seed-crop has been by identification of symptoms in the growing crop during visual inspections. These assessments are now backed-up in target crops by virus detection in the daughter (seed) tubers and there is an increasing emphasis on the diagnosis of virus infections by using advanced procedures in laboratory-based tests. For example, SCRI in its strategic research has developed a number of important diagnostic tests for virus and bacterial diseases based on serological and molecular biological approaches, and SASA has used these tests and some of its own to examine the health of seed stocks. These new, laboratory-based methods seek to improve sensitivity and effectiveness in detecting all virus strains likely to be encountered. These show how the combination of scientific/technological and regulatory services are continuing to advance the standards of Scottish seed.

FUNGAL AND BACTERIAL DISEASE

Most fungal and bacterial diseases of the potato occur whenever potatoes are grown but the climate is unsuitable for some important fungal diseases such as verticillium wilt, and Scotland enjoys complete freedom from some of the most important bacterial diseases. In particular, the bacterial diseases brown rot and ring rot, caused respectively by Pseudomonas solancearum and Clavibacter michiganensis subsp. sepedonicus, are not found in Scotland. An important cause of soft rots, Erwina chrysanthemi is also absent from Scottish stocks. Until 1992 the Scottish seed industry was protected from the importation of diseases from outside the country by a quarantine system for imported seed. In that year the previous system gave way to the uniform EU system of plant passports enabling the movement of seed equivalent health, even into a High Health region. However, since the recognisation of outbreaks of brown rot elsewhere in Europe, a voluntary ban has been maintained on the importation of seed from continental Europe.

NEMATODES

As in all European countries, land used for production of potato seed-tubers must be free of potato cyst nematode (PCN) and fields to be used for seed production are routinely sampled for cysts before planting. Any fields in which cysts are detected are scheduled and excluded from the certification scheme. Some exported stocks are subject to additional stringent tests on the tubers themselves. As part of the strategy for maintaining the high health status of Scottish seed potatoes, the Scottish seed-certification scheme insists on long rotations between seed crops; a minimum period of six years being mandatory, and periods of 9 years between potato crops are common. This helps to ensure that PCN nematodes are not a problem in Scottish stocks and also helps to minimize the build-up of fungal pathogens.

SHORTENED PRODUCTION CYCLES.

The high health-status of seed potatoes production in Scotland is recognized by the EU in that all of Scotland is included as part of a High Health region for seed potato production. The Virus Tested Stem Cutting (VTSC) scheme ensures that virus-free material, either as stem cuttings or microtubers, enters at the top of the certification scheme each year, providing a regular flow of clean material through the system.

The length of the production cycle from pre-basic seed to seed for commercial ware crops is determined by economics and the multiplication rates of the intermediate generations. Micropropagation methods have been adopted uniformly in the maintenance and storage of new cultivars and the technology has been simplified and developed commercially, so that micropropagation and minituber production are now widely used for the rapid production of larger quantities of virus-free, pre-basic seed. Minitubers produced in protected, soil-free conditions are supplied by the SOAEFD or by commercial companies, depending upon the cultivars, and it has been estimated that up to seventy percent of the Scottish seed crop originated in a test tube. The widespread use of minitubers has allowed a reduction of several years in the generation cycle from pre-basic seed to commercial quantities of seed at prices suited for ware production. Buyers of Scottish seed-tubers obtain planting material with a shorter history of field-based production than was the case only a few years ago. This development results in lower costs and better assurance of freedom from soil-borne fungal and bacterial diseases and contact-transmitted viruses such as potato virus X.

AGRONOMIC ADVANCES.

Most potato crops in Scotland are grown in stone-separated soil. This practice allows harvesting with minimum amounts of scuffing and bruising and so reduces the opportunity for ingress of diseases such as dry rot (Fusarium spp.) and gangrene (Phoma exigua). The use of lower levels of fertilizer, particularly N, than in ware-growing regions advances maturity in the crops.

Seed-crops are killed early, usually in August, limiting further the opportunities for disease, both aphid- and soil-borne. There is extensive and increasing use of modern, clean storage facilities with well-regulated temperature and humidity conditions. The spread of such facilities has been encouraged by extension work by SAC and by indigenous commercial companies specialising in atmosphere control in stores.

The physiological age of seed-tubers is recognised as an important characteristic modifying the potential performance of daughter crops. As seed tubers develop in store they progress through and out of dormancy and tubers of most cultivars will have broken their innate or inherent dormancy by mid-January. Thereafter, the development of sprouts is normally prevented by the low temperatures used in storage, a period of 'imposed' dormancy. During this period of imposed dormancy, tubers will change from being apically-dominant, tending to produce one or few sprouts, to non-apically-dominant, tending to produce several sprouts when transferred to conditions favouring growth. Growers who wish to use pre-sprouted, apically-dominant seed for the production of early crops should ask for delivery of their seed early so that they can control for themselves the development of sprouts on the seed-tuber by established methods. Normally seed-tubers would be supplied unsprouted and not apically dominant.

Where a customer wishes seed-tubers that have come out of dormancy and are suited for planting at a different time of year from the usual in the higher northern latitudes then he should consider the possibilities offered by minitubers that can be produced outside the normal seasonal cycle (see earlier).

Seed-tuber size interacts with cultivar and planting density in a complex way to influence the population density of tubers in the daughter crop and, so, the size-grade distribution in that crop at any given yield. These interactions have been captured in a seed-rate programme, developed at SCRI and used by SAC in Scotland and by ADAS in England and Wales, that allows a grower to optimize the combination of seed-size and planting rate. Formerly potato seed-tubers were marketed in a single range of size, 35 - 55 mm diameter. Now, customers should be able to find seed suppliers who are willing to quote prices for seed in more closely specified sizes and smaller sizes, and some may be prepared to supply seed-tubers by number.

BREEDING NEW VARIETIES.

The aim of potato breeding at SCRI is the development of scientific breeding methods. New cultivars are produced as by-products of this programme to demonstrate that the methods work in practice and to transfer the benefits of the advances in disease resistance, quality and yield to the public at large and to growers in particular. The release of new cultivars from the breeding research programme is done principally through two consortia of commercial companies. In addition, through its own commercial arm, Mylnefield Research Services Ltd. (MRS), SCRI undertakes targeted breeding programmes for other companies at full economic costs. The successes achieved by the former Scottish Plant Breeding Station and the present SCRI can be gauged from the steady stream of 56 new cultivars produced, including the widely-grown Craigs and Pentland series and, most recently, the new crisping cultivar Brodick, with resistance to low-temperature sweetening, and two table cultivars Buchan and Brodie.

Access to the genetic diversity in the Commonwealth Potato Collection and the development of cell- and molecular-based techniques such as somatic fusion and marker-assisted selection offer the promise of more rapid incorporation of characters such as blight-, nematode-, and virus-resistance from wild species into agronomically superior clones and cultivars.

Micropropagation systems are highly productive. For instance, starting from one shoot tip over one and a quarter million clonal copies can be generated in a single year, and the use of sterile media and enhanced growth conditions allow not only year-round production but, also, the programmed production of material for precise dates without any influence of climate or growing season. Thus, the application of tissue culture and micropropagation to potato breeding programmes can shorten dramatically the time taken between the production of a particular genotype and its presentation as a candidate new cultivar in National List Trials

FOR THE FUTURE

Studies currently under way at SCRI, often in collaboration with other Scottish organisations, on the ecology of aphid- and soil-borne viruses are designed to lead to still-better control strategies. Enhancement of the resistance of potato germplasm to viruses is being achieved by both conventional breeding and genetic manipulation. Thus, the SCRI potato breeding programme has incorporated very high levels of resistance to PVX and PVY into its breeding lines. These techniques are currently being used to develop potato lines with greatly improved resistance to PLRV and potato mop-top virus. Similarly advances are being made incorporating resistance to late blight (Phytophthora infestans) and PCN and in the development of resistance to low-temperature sweetening in potatoes stored for processing. The search for and development of advanced detection methods continues, based on recombinant and nucleic acid technologies.

NOW

The strengths of the Scottish seed-industry derive from the people, the organisations, and the climate of Scotland. Scottish seed producers are among the most advanced and dedicated of potato growers. Their skills are continually being developed through exchanges with the research and extension bases provided by SCRI, SAC, and SASA, and the maintenance of standards is monitored and assured by the Seed Potato Inspectorate. The size and geographic proximity of the several organisations ensure close integration that benefits both the seed potato seed industry and its customers.

SCOTTISH SEED CERTIFICATION SCHEME

Seed Potatoes must be produced and marketed in Scotland in accordance with a statutory classification scheme administered by the Scottish Office Agriculture, Environment & Fisheries Department. The requirements laid down for the scheme are well within the minimum requirements for the basic category set down in the EC Directive for the Marketing of Seed Potatoes, they also meet the requirements of the EEC Grades and of other EC Directives in respect of plant health matters. An outline of the scheme is as follows:

a. Land - soil from the land must have been tested and no trace of Potato Cyst Nematode (Globodera rosochiensis or pallida) found; Wart Disease (Synchytrium endobioticum) must not have occured at any time on the land and no potatoes must have been grown in the land for the preceding 5 years.

b. Growing Season Inspection - all seed potato crops produced in Scotland are derived from tubers and micro plants, which are grown and tested by the Department to ensure freedom from viruses and from certain fungi and bacteria that can be latent in tubers Pre-basic stocks must be 100% pure and true to type with NIL tolerance for disease. The basic category is divided into 3 classes - Virus Tested Stem Cuttings (VTSC) wih a maximum of 2 generations; Super Elite (SE) and Elite (E) both with a maximum of 3 generations. VTSC Stocks must be 100% pure and true to type and have a NIL tolerance for disease. Super Elite and Elite crops must be 99.95% pure and true to type with the following tolerances for diseases:-

	Super Elite	Elite
	%	%
Severe Mosaic	NIL	{ 0.5% including only
Leafroll	0.01	{ 0.1% Leafroll and/or
Mild Mosaic	0.05	{ severe mosaic
Blackleg	0.25	

There is a further class in the basic category called class AA. This is a "catch" class at which crops entered for the higher classes may be certified if they fail to meet the above requirements but where the crop is still relatively free from disease. AA class crops must be 99.9% pure and true to type: they have a combined maximum tolerance of 1.0 for severe mosaic, and a tolerance for Blackleg. AA Class crops are not permitted to be planted in the GB Protected Region for seed potato production.

Compliance with these requirements is checked by a team of SOAFED officers. Crops are visited at 2 week intervals from shortly after emergence until the haulm has been destroyed. A minimum of 2 formal inspections are carried out to determine the class of the crop and checks made to ensure that good husbandry practices, in particular control of virus vectors, is being carried out. Failure to control virus vectors results a post-harvest test for that crop. In all a total of some 25-30,000 inspections are made of the 15,000 ha or so grown.

c. Tuber Inspection - Classified seed potatoes must be officially labelled and sealed. A copy of the official label currently in use appears below. Official labels are issued only by SOAEFD and sealing of the container is achieved either by machine stitching a label into a sack or incorporating a tie-hole label into the cover of a box, a bag or the outlet from a bulker. In all cases the official label will be affixed in such a way that it will be obvious if the container has been tampered with. If a container does not carry such an official label it does not contain classified seed potatoes. All lots of classified seed potatoes are inspected after grading to ensure that the above procedures have been followed and that the tubers meet the prescribed standards. The tolerances allowed at tuber inspection are the same for SE, E and AA classes but are of a higher standard for VTSC. All classes, though, must have a NIL tolerance for quarantine pests and diseases. For the lower classes a maximum of 0.5% is applied to all rots with a 1% tolerance for the individual diseases. Skin Spot, Powdery and Common Scab and Black Scurf have a combined maximum of 4%, with lower individual tolerances in all cases except for Common Scab. Where surface diseases are involved tubers are considered infected by these diseases if, in the case of Skin Spot and Powdery Scab one eighth or more of the surface is affected (except for the cankerous form of the latter which is always counted) and, in the case of Black Scurf and Common Scab one quarter or more of the surface is affected; in both cases at least 2 eyes at the rose end must be unaffected. External blemishes or misshapen tubers have a tolerance maximum of 2% and soil or other matters must not exceed 1%; outsizes must not exceed 2% by weight and impurities 0.1% by number.

EEC-PLANT PASSPORT	SCOTLAND (U.K.)
	BASIC SEED POTATOES
SPECIES	SOLANUN TUBEROSUM
PRODUCERS NO.	141385010
REGISTRATION NO.	UK/S/
VARIETY	MARIS PIPER
GRADE SE2	**CLASS**
SIZE	35 x 55 mm
DATE OF	
CLOSING	27/2/96 **NET. WT.**
ZP-UK,IRL,P(AZORES),DK	**A 0000000**
EEC RULES AND STANDARDS	

HOW CODE IS MADE UP :

Producer No.   Crop No.

1 4 1 3 8 5 0 1 0 1

AREA   FIELD

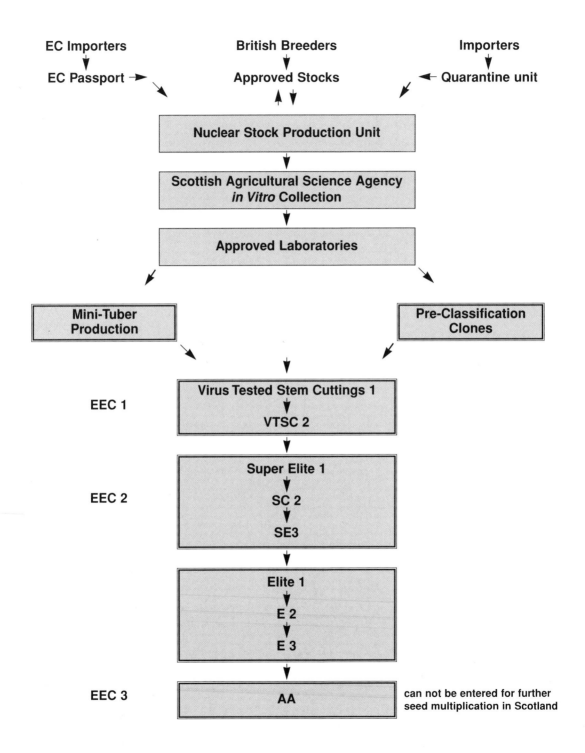

EC Importers
EC Passport →

British Breeders
Approved Stocks

Importers
← Quarantine unit

Nuclear Stock Production Unit

Scottish Agricultural Science Agency
in Vitro Collection

Approved Laboratories

Mini-Tuber
Production

Pre-Classification
Clones

EEC 1

Virus Tested Stem Cuttings 1
VTSC 2

EEC 2

Super Elite 1
SC 2
SE3

Elite 1
E 2
E 3

EEC 3

AA

can not be entered for further
seed multiplication in Scotland

Chapter IV

Diseases

BLACKLEG

Blackleg is due to the bacterium Erwinia Carotovora Var Atroseptica. Early in the season the foliage of an affected plant turns yellow due to the stems rotting at the base which turns black. Although occasionally one or two healthy stems develop, the plant is most likely to die before any tubers reach maturity. However in any that have already developed the flesh will show a brown-grey slimy rot which will start at the heel end of the tuber. All infected plants should be dug out and destroyed, burned if possible. If severely infected tubers are stored they will decay but those only slightly infected may show no symptoms and if planted will introduce further infection in the following season. Plants showing signs of disease should be rogued out where possible. Only a few plants in any one crop are likely to be Blackleg infected since the disease usually occurs as a result of planting infected tubers. Healthy tubers can be infected at harvesting time through direct contact with a diseased tuber, therefore once the disease has appeared the rest of the crop should be carefully harvested and only healthy tubers stored. The disease does not spread from plant to plant in the field or garden and there is little risk of the soil becoming contaminated unless there are large numbers of the bacteria present and the ground is very wet.

BLIGHT

Blight disease is caused by the fungus Phytophthora Infestans and is the most serious disease to attack the potato crop as it can infect the leaves, stems and tubers. The first symptoms are the appearance of brown-black patches on the leaves and stems. The disease spreads rapidly - it first destroys the top growth completely then moves to the tubers destroying them. The disease is most prevalent in dry warm weather when the patches become dry and brown. When wet the blotches spread and the leaves and stems turn black and quickly rot. Masses of white fungal threads develop on the under-surfaces of the leaves and produce spores which are wind-borne or washed down by rain into the soil and infect haulms and tubers at soil level.

Tubers show a red brown rot under the skin which spreads inwards destroying the tubers completely. To prevent an infection the crop should be sprayed at 10 day intervals with a reliable blight spray. Should the crop become infected the remedy is to cut off the foliage at almost ground level at first signs of the infection. This is not a 100% cure but some tubers can be saved which are still edible. Tubers from a Blight infected crop should not be saved for planting. There are a number of potato varieties on the market which have some resistance to Blight.

DRY ROT

Dry Rot is a common name of a disease which is caused by Fusarium Funga and is a disease which occurs in storage. It normally develops from January onwards. Though called Dry Rot, infected tubers are anything but dry: usually affected tubers succumb to other nasties like bacteria and tubers break down to form a slimy smelly mess which bears no resemblance to a healthy tuber. The first symptom is a shrivelling of the skin at one end of the tuber followed by a rapid shrinking of the affected tissues. The typical symptoms can be described as brown lesions in the flesh developing from a point of injury. The margin of the rot is diffuse and merges into the healthy part of the tuber in contrast to the distinct edge of a gangrene lesion due to shrinkage. The skin develops concentric wrinkles, cavities develop in the tissue and white-pink fungal pustules form on the surface. Typical symptoms are most likely to be found in infected tubers stored at low humidity. Dry Rot attacks tubers via wounds or other forms of injury. Infection may be due to injury at harvest time, the fungus entering through the eyes, breathing pores, scab wounds or abrasions. Prevent wounds by treating your potatoes carefully at lifting time or when storing, which should be done in a frost-proof, but cool, dry and well ventilated place as the disease is favoured by damp, warm 16°C/61°F airless conditions. When purchasing seed potatoes take them out of the bags on delivery and place them in sprouting trays for garden plantings.

SKIN SPOT

Skin spot (Polyscytalum pustulans) attacks all underground parts and causes superficial pimples on the tuber; it also attacks eyes and sprouts. That can lead to non-emergence in some instances. Pimples are often surrounded by dark sunken rings, generally superficial, but occasionally deeper under cold conditions. It develops gradually during storage and may be confused with non-erupting scabs of powdery scab, but tissue may be completely killed. Blackening and withering of sprouts under damp conditions can encourage the production of dense white mould. The outer layers of the roots turn brown and may break away. The disease is encouraged by wet conditions at lifting time and cold conditions early in storage. No varieties are fully resistant to skin spot. It is beneficial to box and sprout seed early. Early blind tubers should be discarded, seed stored in dry conditions and cured at 16°-18°C, 60°-65°F for a few days.

After lifting it is recommended that Organo-Mercurial Dips, Systematic Fungicides, Thiabengasole, Benomyl, Fumigant 2 and Aminobutane have given good control in storage. Fumigant must be applied within two weeks of lifting.

Note, that all chemicals are not cleared for use on ware potatoes for human consumption.

SILVER SCURF

Silver Scurf (Helminthosporium Solani) is a common tuber skin blemish which detracts from appearance and can cause excessive dehydration and consequent shrivelling. Symptoms are of a silvery appearance of dead skin under damp conditions. Black spore-bearing structures give a sooty like appearance and skin may eventually flake off when tubers become dehydrated. Infection can come from infected seed. The soil and warm moist conditions can encourage spread. Disease is prevented at temperatures below 30°C (38°F), but losses through dehydration may be high. There are no potato varieties resistant to Silver Scurf. Avoid planting severely affected seed tubers.

INTERNAL BROWNING

Symptoms are generally confined to a browning of the central pith tissue. It may be an early stage in hollow heart development or it may be associated with mineral deficiencies. Causes are not fully understood and no proven control methods are known to date.

BLACKHEART

The disorder occurs in storage as a blackened area in the central pith tissue of the tuber. Dead tissue does not smell and the cause is oxygen starvation. Usually due to an overheated store, control is by normal temperature control in storage.

SECOND GROWTH

The symptoms are excessive protuberances at the eyes. There may also be a development of small tubers called chain tubers. Attached by a length of stolon, others may elongate producing a "dolly" effect. Second growth is most likely to occur during good weather conditions or wet weather, following dry conditions. Control can be partially achieved through the use of irrigation to regulate water supply and by earlier haulm destruction.

JELLY END ROT

The stolon end of the tuber becomes soft and translucent, but the skin remains intact. The internal tissues do not smell and don't stain blue in the presence of iodine. The most common cause is reabsorption of starch as sugar into the plant – this is more common under dry conditions. Control through irrigation to regulate water supply.

STEM END AND VASCULAR BROWNING

A brown to blackish area at the point of the stolon attachment which may extend into the vascular ring sometimes develops when the haulms are killed off rapidly by chemicals in somewhat dry soil conditions. The browning may be caused by excessive amounts of fertiliser treatments. Vascular browning alone giving a netted appearance if cut tangentially may result from other unknown causes.

BLACK SCURF AND STEM CANKER

Black Scurf and Stem Canker (Rhizoctonia Solani) is a black scurfy condition of the skin which detracts from appearance. Sprouts and stem bases may be attacked, brown to black particles of variable shape and size are easily detached from the skin with one's thumb nail. Sprout tips are blackened causing secondary sprouts to grow which in turn can be infected and sprouts may not emerge under severe attacks. Stem bases bear brown cankers which may girdle the stems and may cause rolling, wilting and formation of aerial tubers, distinguished from leafroll virus by the presence of stem cankers, can also be distinguished from blackleg sometimes by the absence of blackness on stems at ground level. A superficial white powdery collar may develop just above the ground level. Seed and soil borne infections are more frequent on light soils and under cold dry conditions, no potato varieties are resistant to black scurf and stem canker. Well sprouted seed is best used and early planting in cold conditions should be avoided. Avoid planting badly infected seed.

INTERNAL RUST SPOT

Discrete brown spots appear randomly distributed throughout. The tuber is sometimes rather difficult to distinguish from some forms of Spraing. No particular conditions have been consistently found to promote the disorder. This disease occurs within the flesh, much like Spraing, except that the brown marks are scattered through the flesh when the affected tuber is cut open; the exact cause of the trouble is not known but is thought to be a physiological disorder. Symptoms can be less severe in a crop when even growth is maintained throughout the growing season by preventing any checks due to sudden drying out of the soil, incorporating lots of humus into the soil prior to planting and keeping the crop irrigated in dry seasons where possible. If you find that internal Rust Spot is a problem, varieties with some resistance to Rust Spot should be grown.

GANGRENE

Gangrene is a storage disease which is caused by fungus Phoma Solanicola Foveata and can be present in most soils. It may occur on healthy tubers but normally only affects tubers that have been damaged, particularly at harvesting time and especially if the soil is very wet at that time. Other causes can be by mechanical damage at grading time when storing at low temperatures. Washing potatoes can cause gangrene by storing wet tubers in cold conditions. Washing seed potatoes is not recommended, but should they be washed make sure that tubers are thoroughly dried and stored at the right temperature. 45°F/7°C to 50°F/10°C is about correct for potatoes. The diseased area enlarges until most of the tuber is decayed and shrunken. If cut open at this stage it will be hollow and rotten inside. Do handle your potatoes carefully and store them in proper storage conditions as a precaution against the disease. Gangrene can occur in new seed after delivery depending on one's own storage conditions, such as setting up tubers for chitting in a cold greenhouse with low temperatures. Some potato varieties are susceptible to gangrene. Others have some resistance to the disease, but severely decayed tubers and less damaged seed can be planted by cutting out the damaged parts. The disease is unlikely to spread once planted.

WATERY WOUND ROT

Watery wound is a rot following wounding but is not of major economic importance. The Tuber skins become discoloured and often stretch around infection point. Internally the central tissue becomes wet and pulpy and cavities develop. The outer flesh may remain firm. Secondary bacteria readily invade the affected tissue. Early harvesting in hot dry weather conditions encourages infection. Premature lifting in hot weather is best avoided to minimise mechanical damage.

PINK ROT (PHYTOPHTHORA ERYTHROSEPTICA)

A characteristic rot that develops from the heel end of the tuber, it is not regarded as a major economic importance. Wilting of the foliage may occur. Tubers become slightly discoloured, but remain fairly firm and exude a sticky liquid to which soil adheres. Internally the affected tissue after exposure to air turns pink, then purple, and eventually a dark brown with a characteristic smell. Infection from soil conditions is most preva-

lent in dry hot summers and although no varieties are resistant to the disease, good drainage and good rotation can help to curb the disease. There are no chemical cures.

HOLLOW HEART

A disorder that develops in potato crops which have suffered from drought conditions and have then been irrigated. Similarly a long wet spell following dry weather can cause hollow centres in the tubers and large cracks also appear. These troubles can be partly reduced by watering early crops at least 10-14 day intervals when tubers start to form. But watering should be reduced when tubers are nearing maturity as water will do more harm than good at this stage and can encourage growth cracks. Much the same procedure applies to maincrops. Water potato crops regularly in dry weather (if possible) since it is important that the soil is never allowed to dry out completely.

COMMON SCAB

Common Scab (Streptomyces) causes superficial raised scabs affecting the tuber skins only. In severe cases the whole surface can become infected, resulting in considerable wastage when the tubers are peeled for cooking. Common Scab can be caused by high lime content in the soil and by fresh farmyard manure, such as pig manure, which is best avoided for potato crops. Sandy or gravelly soils and lack of water can encourage Common Scab. Plenty of peat leafmould should be incorporated into light sandy soils for water retention. Irrigation is beneficial during the growing season in severely infected soils. Varieties with some Scab resistance should be grown.

POWDERY SCAB

Powdery Scab (also known as Corky Scab) is caused by the fungus Spongospora Subter-ranea. This is a more serious scab which causes round swellings around the tuber eyes, eventually the scabs bursting open, releasing a brown mass of powdery spores which can contaminate the soil. The disease is only likely to be really troublesome in a wet season, or on low-lying wet soils and where potatoes have been grown too often. Susceptible varieties should not be grown in a garden where the disease has occurred. However, potato crops have been grown in soils, following a Powdery Scab outbreak, without a recurrence. There are a number of potato varieties on the market with high resistance to powdery scab.

LEAF ROLL AND SPRAING

Leafroll and Spraing are virus infections. Leafroll is the most common in the potato crop, easily recognised by the curling leathery leaves. The plants are undersized and tubers are few and small. The disease is carried in tubers from infected plants of the previous year. Seed should not be saved from an infected crop. Plants should be dug out and burned. Spraing is caused by tobacco rattle virus, less frequently by potato mop-top virus. The flesh of affected tubers show red-brown lesions, which have a wavy or arc like appearance in cross section. If these tubers are used for seed, a mottling of the stems or leaves will appear on the developing plants. Tobacco rattle virus is transmitted by certain free-living eelworms present in the soil, which are distinct from the potato cyst eelworm. Therefore, it is always best to grow potatoes on a fresh site after an incident of this disease has occurred. Weeds in which the virus can over winter should be controlled.

WART DISEASE

Few gardeners have seen wart disease. It is caused by the fungus Synchytrium Endobioticum. The warts are small, white growths which appear round the eyes of the tubers in June/July, and in wet conditions they appear round the base of the haulm. These proliferate until they resemble black cauliflower like curds, often larger than the tuber which they attack. The far smaller cankers of Powdery Scab with which it can be confused are brown (not black), and appear also on the fine roots as well as the tubers, the spores of this less serious disease can last up to 6-7 years in the soil, but those of Wart Disease can last at least thirty years or more. The resting spores of Wart Disease can pass through a pig's digestive system, spreading infection in pig manure, so do avoid using pig manure for potato growing.

Wart Disease can travel just as easily on tyres, horses' hooves, through the air, from mud-smeared roads and even your own boots from one allotment to the other. Once a single spore finds a non-immune potato plot, a chain of infection starts.

Wart disease was first observed in England in 1902 but was confused with Powdery Scab until 1909, when it was described and named in an article in the Gardeners' Chronicle. The then Board of Agriculture took action under the Destructive Insects and Pests act of 1907, and made the symptoms noticeable. It reduced the Powdery Scab to its modern low levels by advising its simple cure by crop rotation. The source of any outbreak of Wart Disease was tracked down to certain infected areas, to which they confined the outbreak. There are immune and non-immune potato varieties. An important consideration to be taken into account when buying or ordering seed potatoes is the area where you will be planting. One must choose immune varieties if you live in a Wart Disease area. Your local Department of Agricultural and Fisheries will advise you whether your area is immune or non-immune.

BLACK DOT
(Colletotrichum Coccodes)

A weak pathogen usually senescent tissue or plants weakened by some other cause. However the fungus may form profuse microsclerotia on the tuber surface detracting from the market value of the potato crop.

Symptoms are a dark brown-grey blemish over the tuber surface which can be similar in appearance to Silver Scurf (Helminthosporium Solani) but with more irregularly shaped lesions with less well defined edges . Black microsclerotia just visible to the naked eye often give the tubers a sooty appearance which can develop into a silvery sheen in storage.

Stems roots and stolons can also be infected giving rise to wilt symptoms, but this is uncommon in the U.K. where infection is mostly limited to senescent tissue.

Infection is from both infected tubers and soil where the fungus is widespread as it survives on plant debris. Between host crops, development on the infected tubers is favoured by wet growing conditions and may be encouraged by irrigation. Symptoms on tubers may develop in store and is favoured by warm moist conditions. Some varieties can be more susceptible than others to Black Dot. Severely affected seed should be avoided. Harvest early and maintain cool, dry storage conditions. There are chemicals available that may reduce the spread to progeny tubers but will not control infection from soil inoculum.

LITTLE POTATO

Little potato is the premature formation of small tubers directly from the seed tuber without any foliage development. The causes are generally associated with over advanced sprout development: e.g. seed with advanced long sprouts planted into unfavourable growing conditions. Some varieties are more prone to this disorder than others. Never oversprout your seed. Some gardeners set seed in trays as early as November. This is nonsense and is not recommended.

COILED SPROUT

The emerging sprout may be distorted and coiled a number of times before emergence. The causes are very similar to those of Little Potato, such as over sprouting together with over compaction of the ridges at planting time.

FROST DAMAGE

This is a frequent problem with seed consignments which travel in frosty weather. Symptoms vary according to exposure time and temperature. Tubers do not actually freeze until the temperature drops below about -2°C (29°F) freezing. This results in a wet external appearance after thawing which may cause wet patches on seed bags. There is no smell at first but, under warm conditions, unpleasant smelling wet rots develop. Under cold, dry conditions flesh will become mealy. If only one side of the tuber is frozen this sometimes becomes sharply divided from the unaffected zone by a brown curck line. Chilling is usually only visible after cutting. There are two types of symptom: (A) vascular discolouration – the ring of vascular tissue is approximately ¼″ below the surface becomes blackened and blackening extends to fine vascular strands on either side giving a spotted appearance if cut straight or a netted appearance if cut on the slant; (B) flesh discolouration – irregular blue grey to black patches appear. Tubers tend to shrivel but this may be due to other causes like silver scurf. Precautions should be taken never to expose tubers to temperatures below 0°C (32°F). Avoid movement of potatoes if freezing is suspected as this will minimise the injury. Avoid planting seed showing signs of chilling injury as eyes may be affected and cause spacing.

WITCHES BROOM

Extensive tests over the past 40-50 years have shown that the virus is widely distributed but usually rare in commercial crops. Occasionally, particularly in a season following a hot dry summer, Witches Broom is locally prevalent and it has been inferred that it is introduced to potatoes by a vector – migrating from herbage. Circumstantial evidence indicates a leafhopper vector but the exact identity either of vector or of primary host is yet unknown, except in cases of epidemic infiltration to parts of crops. The disease is of no economic significance. The infection is perpetuated in the tubers but these tend to be small and are gradually eliminated from the stock. The Witches Broom disease, as known in the U.K., is similar to but nevertheless distinct from diseases of the same name occurring in Canada and Central Europe. Tests have shown that Witches Broom is a condition quite distinct from that of Wilding A (genetical variation) with which it has often been confused.

CUCUMBER MOSAIC

The Cucumber Mosaic virus has been noted occasionally in Scotland in potato crops. This virus has not been found in commercial stocks but only in gardens where potatoes have been grown close to infected perennial hosts of the virus. Cucumber Mosaic is very rare.

Chapter V

Pests

EELWORM

Potato Eelworm can be a very serious pest indeed. Cysts can lie dormant in the soil for many years and when a potato crop is planted on infested ground, the larvae attack the potato plant roots producing plant sickness. The affected plants become black. First signs of the disease is when parts of the tubers become soft and stunted and pale green to yellow. Plants wilt easily and eventually die off when immature. Tuber production will be very small when Eelworms are present. There will be small dots on the roots which later become orange/brown in colour. Infected plants and tubers should be destroyed (burned if possible). Do not leave infected plants lying around. Potato crops should not be planted on infected soil for at least 8 years with the exception of the recent Eelworm Resistant varieties. For many years it was thought that only one type of potato cyst Eelworm existed, the one known as Globodera Rostochiensis or the Golden Eelworm (after the colour of the cysts). Modern plant breeders produced several potato varieties that were resistant to this pest and these proved to be most useful in many Eelworm infested soils but not all. It was eventually discovered that the occasional failures were due to the presence of a second species of Eelworm, the Pale Eelworm (Globodera Pallida) which was able to attack varieties that were resistant to the Golden Eelworm.

List of Eelworm Resistant Varieties

Early	*	(Maincrop)	*
Accent FE	1989	Alwara EM	1986
Adora FE	1989	Antar LM	1987
Aminca FE	1977	Atlantic EM	1992
Ausonia	1981	Avondale LM	1982
Balmoral SE	1989	Cara LM	1976
Berber SE	1985	Cultra EM	1986
Costella SE	1985	Diamant EM	1982
Concorde FE	1988	Fianna EM	1988
Dundrum SE	1983	Jewel EM	1985
Dunrod FE	1987	Karama LM	1993
Fronika SE	1985	Kingston LM	1981
Heather SE	1993	Maris Piper EM	1967
Junior FE	1990	Maxine EM	1993
Kestrel SE	1992	Morene EM	1983
Lady Rosetta SE	1988	Morag EM	1985
Liseta SE	1989	Navan EM	1987
Minerva FE	1988	Nicola EM	1973
Nadine SE	1987	Obelix EM	1989
Pentland Javelin FE	1969	Panda EM	1986
Penta SE	1983	Red Cara LM	1981
Premiere FE	1985	Sante EM	1985
Rocket FE	1987	Saturna EM	1964
Saxon SE	1992	Stamina EM	1992
Sperrin SE	1988	Stemster EM	1986
Stroma SE	1989	Slaney EM	1991
Swift FE	1993	Toledo EM	1988
Timate SE	1989	Tristar EM	1993
Winston FE	1992	Valor EM	1993

FE - First Early; SE - Second Early; EM - Early Maincrop;
LM - Late Maincrop; * Year of Introduction

The Pale Eelworm is much less common than the Golden Eelworm but both exist in the same field or garden. Golden Eelworm resistant varieties are very useful in Eelworm infected soils but the first time they are grown there might be some reduction in cropping as the Eelworm is still able to feed on the plants, but as it is unable to reproduce, the number of cysts in the soil it is reduced dramatically. Soil can be tested for Eelworm. It is not advisable to plant potatoes preceding fruit, chrysanthemums or herbaceous crops as these plants can be Eelworm infected contaminating the soil. One should plant certified seed stock at all times. Tubers given by a friend or neighbour can be Eelworm infected and can contaminate your garden. Eelworms do not bore holes in potato tubers. Slugs are mistaken for Eelworm by many gardeners.

THE TOMATO MOTH
(Lacanobia Oleracea)

It is well established that the moth attacks tomatoes and cucumbers indoors and carnations and chrysanthemums and brassicas outdoors. Recently they have been known to attack the potato crop. It also feeds on weeds such as docks and goosefoot etc. Damage to potatoes is not common, but when the moth is present damage can be very severe. Moths can emerge from over-wintered pupae in May-June and eggs are laid in batches from 50 - 300 on the underside of leaves. The eggs hatch within two weeks, and after initially feeding in groups, the caterpillars disperse and feed singly, eating potato leaves down to a skeleton of the leaf margins. Inwards larval development can last up to 30 - 40 days after which the caterpillars pupate over winter. The moths emerge again the following season. The caterpillars are variable in colour from dark brown to a pale green and tend to be mottled with many white spots and usually have a yellow line running the full length of the body on each side. When fully grown they can be $1^{3}/_{4}''$ (4cm) in length. As eggs are laid in large batches on the leaves initial damage by the young caterpillars is patchy, but when they start to disperse the damage can spread rapidly from one plant to another, normally along the potato drills, leaving only the stems. Attacks such as this tend to be local and sporadic if the caterpillars are detected early in the season. By checking leaves in June for groups of small caterpillars a single insecticide spray should control the caterpillars before they can inflict much damage to the crop. Insecticides such as aphid-borne virus sprays should control tomato moth caterpillars.

SLUG DAMAGE

The most common slug to attack potato tubers is the Keel Slug which bores holes in the tubers. Comparatively small holes are made in the outside of the potato but the inside can be so extensively tunnelled it may become completely hollow. Slugs generally attack the tubers from mid to late season. Early varieties often escape damage, being lifted early in the season. In ground known to have a slug problem, main crop varieties should be lifted as soon as matured in order to minimise the damage. Store damaged tubers separately, as they are liable to develop storage diseases. No potato varieties are resistant to slug damage, but many recent introductions have good resistance to slugs. Crops near to grassland are more likely to be attacked by slugs. The use of organic fertilisers can attract slugs and is best avoided in slug infested soils. Most types of slugs that attack potato tubers spend nearly all of their lives below the surface level where slug pellets cannot reach them. They do come to the surface occasionally, in warm weather, after periods of heavy rain or during irrigation. Slug pellets should be extensively used at this time.

WIREWORM

Wireworm (Agriotes Spp) are the larvae of click beetles, they occur in large numbers in weed infested areas or under grassland. These pests can cause much trouble by boring into potato tubers. They are a particular problem in wet conditions and often occur in freshly dug pasture or wasteland where they can cause damage for three to four years after the land has been brought into cultivation. Wireworm are thin orange-brown larvae of up to 1″ long. They have three pairs of small legs, but these stiff-bodied insects only move around occasionally. The holes that they make in the tuber are approximately $1/8$″ diameter. But, although they may penetrate deeply, the tubers do not become hollowed out as occurs with slug damage. If your soil is wireworm infected it is an advantage to grow early potato varieties as

they are lifted sooner, before wireworms become fully active. If maincrop varieties are grown, damage can be limited by harvesting the crop as soon as tubers have matured. Do not leave over matured tubers too long in the ground when soil is infected by wireworm.

APHIDS OR GREENFLY

Aphids or greenfly can infest potato leaves during mid to late summer. Some types can spread virus diseases via their mouthparts, which can be very serious to the seed producer or the gardener who wishes to save his own seed as aphids can spread virus infections very quickly. Potato crops should be sprayed with an aphid spray at 14 day intervals. Aphids also attack potato sprouts in storage and chittings trays. Sprouts should also be sprayed with an aphid or Jeyes fluid spray. The mixture should be a little weaker than for the mature crop as young sprouts are tender and are easily burned. It is best to do a test spray first on sprouts. Trays should be disinfected before use. Aphids often over-winter on potato sprouts.

COLORADO BEETLE
(Lepinotarsa Decmlineata)

Colorado Beetle is a most serious defoliator of potato and related plants. It occurs throughout much of Europe but has not been found in Britain or Ireland for some time. The beetles are approximately $1/2$″ long and are yellow with black stripes running length ways along the wing cases. The larvae also grow up to $1/2''$ long and are red with two rows of black markings along their sides. Both adults and larvae feed on potato foliage and large numbers can rapidly reduce plants to bare stems. Colorado Beetle has been kept out of the United Kingdom by a combination of inspection of imported potatoes and plant material and prompt action by the Department of Agriculture and Fisheries Department to eliminate outbreaks that have occurred in the past. Should one find insects in the U.K. that they suspect might be the Colorado Beetle they should send specimens in a sealed jar/container to their nearest Department of Agriculture and Fisheries Department, without delay. or inform them of such findings. If insects are found to be the Colorado Beetle the Department of Agriculture takes the necessary steps to eliminate them.

Chapter VI

General Information

Planting Potatoes in the Field
From the 1880's to Date

In the late 1800's potato land was prepared by ploughing, harrowing and grubbing, then drilled by a double-sided plough called a drill plough. It was common in those days to apply farmyard manure in the bottom of the drills which was called manuring in the drill. This was the main fertiliser for growing potatoes in those days. The manure was spread by hand forks and the tubers were planted directly on top of the manure and covered by the drill plough which divided the drills. In the early days of potato growing and until the 1970's potatoes were planted deeper.

Drills were pulled down using a circular harrow. This helped to kill the weeds and expose the young sprouts. They were ridged again later. In those days and until the 1970's potatoes were grubbed and ridged two or three times in the early part of the season with a final ridging-up when the plants were about 9" in height. The circular harrow and grubber are no longer used due to the use of chemical weed sprays. In the late 1940's tractors were rapidly taking over from horses on the farms. Tractor drill ploughs were introduced, which was a frame with three double board ploughs attached. These ploughs were used to make the potato drills. Unfortunately they were unsuitable for covering the planted potatoes because the tractor wheels had to

Top - *Horse drawn potato digging plough from the late 1800's*

Bottom - *Horse drawn circular harrow*

run in the drills, thus damaging the planted seed. However, three cover ploughs were introduced which were fixed to a frame attached to the front of the tractor. These ploughs covered the potatoes which made it possible for the wheels to run between the drills. The covering ploughs being small did not throw enough soil over the planted potatoes so the three bigger ploughs followed on to finish off the job.

Potato planters were invented as early as the beginning of the 1900's but were not very successful. Of course, in those days planters were pulled by horses, then tractor drawn models appeared from time to time. They did not catch on until a more modern three drill model was invented in the 1960's. Three persons were required to operate this model, mainly to feed the tubers into the cups. This type of planter was more popular than previous models and remained in use until the 1980's. Of course the modern planter requires stone separated soil to operate, however, most potatoes are now grown in stone separation soil. The modern potato planters are fully automatic and can handle all sizes of seed. As well as planting the potatoes they apply the fertiliser and can be adjusted to apply different amounts per acre and are fitted with three double sided ploughs to cover the seed. No further cultivating work is carried out on the crop, only weed-blight and insect spraying is done during the growing season, with the haulms burned off prior to harvesting time.

Grading Potatoes

In the late 1800's potatoes were becoming more widely grown and in those early days grading was done by hand. The obvious way to size potatoes was to subject them to riddles with different sized meshes, then feed the tubers into hoppers. They were then directed into light weight barrels for transit to the shops. Seed was sometimes put back into the pits until planting time. Potatoes were sized into three grades, ware, seed and chats. Then about the turn of the century a wooden framed hand operated potato grader was introduced with two iron-meshed riddles, one placed above the other. The top riddle stopped the ware size tubers and let the others through. The second riddle let the chats through and stopped the seed. Again the ware was directed into bags or barrels with the seed retained for planting. Sometimes chats were used as seed by sowing them closely along the drill.

Potato dressing was mixed, with some farmers still using riddles and others operating the hand grader up until the 1940's, when a mechanical potato dresser was introduced, powered by a petrol engine. The potatoes were fed into the dressing machine by hand scoop and separated into ware and seed, then bagged at the rear of the dresser with chats falling through a small chute at the side of the dresser into a basket. This type of dresser became obsolete in the 1980's making way for the large modern graders of today.

Potato Harvesting from the Early Times to the Present

Potato digging by hand fork was a rather slow process, so a horse drawn raiser plough was invented which divided the drill and exposed the tubers, doing much the same job as the hand fork. This only left the gathering of the potatoes to be done by hand. Then a horse drawn spinner digger was invented with a share and spinner with tines. In the

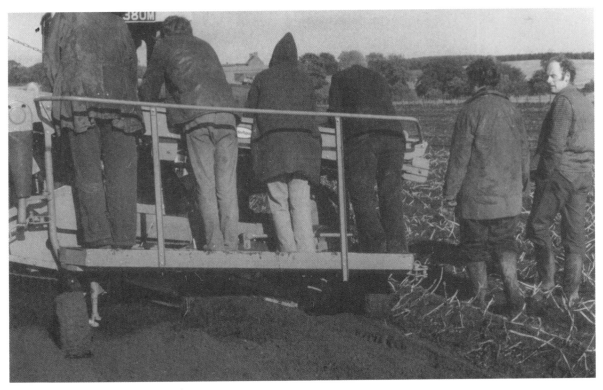

Early Potato Harvester, 1960's

earlier more basic form the horse or tractor drawn potato spinner was supported by two large travelling wheels that provided the power to work the spinner which was mounted on a lengthwise shaft.

Ahead of the spinner, a share was fitted to cut through the earth underneath the drill to loosen the soil and the potatoes so that the prongs on the end of the revolving tines could throw them both to one side. The main success of the spinner depended on the type of soil. Later developments were concerned with adjustments and variations to suit differences in soil. Modern spinners were powered by the tractor, and power lift-ed. Ground wheels were fitted only for guidance and support. The simple spinning tines arrangement spread both earth and tubers over a considerable distance but in heavy clay soils this was the best way to expose the tubers properly.

A screen was fitted to the machine to restrict the distance thrown in lighter soil conditions. The tines were arranged at the same angle in relation to the ground at all points of their travel. This angle could be adjusted but is near vertical. The effect was to give a push to the soil and crop. Rather than swing the mechanism to achieve this it used two wheels with their centres stag-

Two drill elevator digger in operation around 1950's / 1960's

gered, driving the arms carrying the tines. Machines may carry a wheel similar to a plough disc-coulter that cuts ahead of the digger share. Its main purpose was to cut away weeds or other material that may otherwise get caught up in the spinner. This also provides another step to freeing the soil for the spinner.

Elevator Digger

The elevator digger was the successor to the spinner type. The first models were invented in the 1940's. It was a single web one drill digger and was towed and powered by a tractor. A share served the same purpose as on the spinner machine but the earth and potatoes were gathered up on a conveyer belt which was made up of agitated web bars with spaces through which the soil could fall. The potatoes were dropped from the first web onto a rear chain web which deposited them on the ground at the rear of the digger. The machine was sometimes inclined to cover the tubers with haulms. In the late 1950's a double drill elevator digger was introduced: the workings were similar to that of the single drill model, but lifted two drills at once. Then in the 1980's came the introduction of the potato harvester which took over from the potato diggers and potato picking by hand, bringing the end of an era for both.

Potato Pits and Clamps

From the 1800's until the 1970's potatoes were kept in pits 6 ft. to 7 ft. wide by 9" deep. The pit was dug with the excavated earth used for the pit edge. The pit was continued in length as required. The potatoes were tipped from the carts into the pit, then scooped by hand (scoop) into a 4 ft. high triangle shape, then covered by bunched wheat straw and a 12" layer of soil. Less covering may be used in southern parts of the country where frosts are less severe. In more recent times such as the 1960's and 1970's potato clamps were common. These were much bigger than potato pits - straw bales were used for the sides and the top was covered with loose straw.

Clamps only lasted for about twenty years. In the late 1970's large frost-proof storage sheds became popular and took over from the open air pits and clamps. Potatoes were filled in the field into $1/2$ ton and one ton boxes, and then moved by fork lifts. Large potato graders were installed in the storage sheds. Potato boxes are tipped into large hoppers and fed into the grading machines. This system is still in use today - ware potatoes are packed into strong 25kg paper bags and seed in 25 kg. and 50 kg. hessian bags. They are then stacked onto one ton wooden pallets which are loaded onto lorries by fork lifts. Very much different conditions from the days of dressing potatoes at open air pits in extremely cold winter conditions.

Making a potato clamp, 1950's / 1960's

Depositing potatoes in a pit, 1960's

Growing and Storing Potatoes in the Scottish glens – 1800's

In the 1800's and as recently as the 1930's potatoes were not grown in quantity in the Scottish glens mostly because the rough stoney land and hill conditions were unsuitable for potato culture. With the introduction of modern implements more potato crops are now being cultivated in the glens. In earlier times glen farmers only grew potatoes for their own family use and local requirements. The people of the glens depended very much on home grown produce such as milk, flour, oatmeal and potatoes. Potatoes were one of their staple diets.

The potato crop was stored in underground stone built pits known also as a potato house. Some resembled a second world war air raid shelter. The underground storing system was the ideal method, providing secure protection against the severe frost conditions in the high areas of Scotland. The remains of stone pits can still be found in the Angus glen of Glenesk in the north-east of Scotland. Varieties grown in the glens were Duke of York, Up-To-Date, Epicure, Kerr's Pink, Champion, Sharpe's Express, Arran Chief, Great Scot and British Queen.

Lime kiln and tattie pit, Glenesk, Scotland 1860's

Potato Growing During the War Years

During the food shortage of the war years 1939-1945, potatoes were in short supply. To help meet the demand mansion house flower gardens, lawns and leisure parks were cultivated. Potatoes were the most widely grown vegetable of the day.

Tractor drawn potato planter, 1960's

Dividing Tubers

In olden times cutting oversize seed tubers was very popular. Cuts are made from rose end to heel, leaving about equal numbers of eyes on each half of the tuber. This is best done before the sprouts start to appear. Cuts are then sealed by dipping in lime. Tubers can also be cut three quarters from the rose end and left for at least two days, then fully separated by pulling apart. This will avoid the tuber from losing sap. Good results can be obtained by planting cut seed. Varieties with very few eyes are not recommended for this purpose.

Sprouting the Seed

This should be resorted to wherever possible, the results being a longer growing season and a heavier crop. The tubers to be sprouted should be placed in shallow trays or boxes on end, with the eyes upwards. The boxes or trays should be set in a dark position until the tubers begin to sprout, then they should be brought gradually into the light. On receipt of potatoes it is important to unpack them on arrival and store them in a well ventilated place away from danger of frosts.

Potato Market Growers Prices in the 1930's

ABERDEEN 20/11/35.

Samples normal , business fairly good and prices remain firm. Seed in demand for certain varieties. Kerr's Pink Ware – price from growers, delivered in Aberdeen 65/- to 70/- per ton. Wholesale price 4/3d to 4/- to 4/6d per cwt., retail from 9d per stone.

ELGIN 20/11/35.

Slow demand for Kerr's Pink at 70/- to 80/- per ton for local requirements only. No enquiry from the south markets. King Edward and Majestic seed at prices similar to previous weeks but less enquiries.

HADDINGTON 20/11/35.

Great Scot 62/6d. Kerr's Pink at 70/- off Red Soil 90/-, Golden Wonder 66/10d per ton. Seed trade still slow.

MONTROSE 20/11/35.

Trade very slow for both seed and ware but not much on offer. Farmers prepared to hold stocks for improved prices.

PERTH 20/11/35.

Seed Eclipse 105/-, Sharpe's Express 95/-, King Edward 120/-, Doon Star 100/-, Majestic 95/- to 100/-, Arran Banner 100/-, Great Scot 100/-. Ware still a limited trade. White ware 60/-, Kerr's Pink 70/-, Golden Wonder 120/-, King Edward 85/-, all per ton.

Potato grading, Scotland 1950's

Potato grading, Scotland 1950's

ARBROATH 22/11/37.

Ware trade still slow. Not much change in prices for seed. Sharpe's Express 95/-, Eclipse 105/-, King Edward £6.10/-, Majestic and Doon Star £5, all per ton.

EAST LOTHIAN 22/11/37.

Market dull for all varieties on offer, but prices fairly steady. Lifting of the season's crop is almost completed and the tubers deposited in pits. But on some farms blight is prevalent to some extent, while on others there is entire immunity from disease. Doon Star 70/-, Kerr's Pink 70/- to 72/-, Duke of York 85/- to 90/-, Great Scot 65/- to 67/6, Golden Wonders 120/- to 130/-, all per ton.

DUNDEE 23/11/37.

Kerr's Pink 75/-, Great Scot, Majestic and Arran Banner 60/-, Doon Star 65/-, all per ton.

GLASGOW 23/11/37.

Kerr's Pink 75/-, Doon Star 70/-, Golden Wonder 120/-.

BERWICK 22/11/37.

Very little on offer and merchants finding difficulty in getting sufficient supplies. Prices firmer with demand greatly improved, Great Scot 70/-, Majestic 75/-, Kerr's Pink 75/-, Off Red Soil, Great Scot 90/-, all per ton.

CUPAR 23/11/37.

Kerr's Pink 75/-, Great Scot, Majestic and Arran Banner 60/-, Golden Wonder 120/-, all per ton.

EDINBURGH 23/11/37.

Kerr's Pink 70/-, Great Scot 62/6d, Off Red Soil 90/-.

LONDON BOROUGH 22/11/37.

(Potatoes). A satisfactory demand was reported for best samples, but otherwise trading was rather on the quiet side. Supplies were again plentiful and prices were barely steady. Best siltland and light soil King Edward's were quoted at 6/- to 7/-, from dark soil 5/6d to 6/-, Essex and Bedford-shire King Edward's 5/6d to 6/- and Eclipse, Majestic and Doon Star 4/6d to 5/-, all per cwt. Ex-market reports of the potato crop in England and Wales according to the Minis-try of Agriculture and Fisheries show that the quality and condition were generally favourable. The yield per acre over the whole country is forecast at $6^1/_2$ tons which is a $^1/_4$ ton greater than the average forecasts made on November 1st of the ten years 1927 to 1936. The forecast for this year is approximately the same as the average of the final estimates of the 10 years 1926 to 1936 and about a $^1/_4$ ton more than the final production for estimated yield of last year. The total production for this year is forecast at 2,973,000 tons against 2,814,000 tons last year.

Wholesaler to Retailer

The prices per cwt. wholesaler to retailer for the week ended November 20th were as follows:–

Aberdeen – Kerr's Pink 3/9d, Dundee – Kerr's Pink 4/9d, Great Scot and Arran Banner 4/-, Doon Star 4/3d. Edinburgh – Kerr's Pink 4/6d, Great Scot 4/-, Golden

Wonder 7/- (Red Soils 6/-). Glasgow – Kerr's Pink 5/-, Great Scot and Arran Banner. Inverness – Kerr's Pink 4/6d.

New Introductions and Varieties Reinstated to the National List

Before potato varieties can be grown and traded, they must be included on the United Kingdom National Potato List. Exhaustive tests over a number of years are carried out on new introductions wishing to be placed on the U.K. list. If a new variety is first found to fall short of The Department of Agriculture and Fisheries requirements then it will be refused.

However, recent legal changes now permit varieties from another European Community's comparable list to be grown or sold within the U.K. The purpose of listing is to provide some protection to the potato industry against the introduction of a whole range of diseases, while at the same time exercising control. Unfortunately, to keep a variety on the National List a maintenance fee is payable.

To introduce a new variety the following fees are payable: Application Fee, Test Fee, Trial Fee and then a National List Fee for two years entry. Full fees are payable regardless of the variety's popularity. The result is that many old varieties with small demands have disappeared and are still rapidly disappearing from the National List. Any variety can be resurrected, but this is very costly for the grower, and as old varieties cannot be patented this means that once re-introduced to the market, any grower can capitalise on

VARIETIES ALSO KNOWN AS:

America	as	Irish Cobbler
Black Kidney	"	Shetland Black
Blue Potato	"	Foula Black
Blue Grey	"	Blue Fir
Craigneil	"	Russet Kerr's Pink
Delta Star	"	Rode Pipo
Duke of York	"	Mid Lothian Early
Etoile du Nord	"	Rode Star
Evergood	"	Eldorado
Field Marshall	"	Russet Up-to-Date
General	"	President
Jaune de Halland	"	Ideal
Immune Ashleaf	"	Juli
International Kidney	"	Jersey Royal
Keplestone Kidney	"	Rams Horn or Cows Horn
Langworthy	"	White (Golden Wonder)
Liro	"	Linzer Rose
Old Black	"	Blackheart
President	"	P. Kruger
Ratte	"	Asparges
Red Duke of York	"	Rode Eersteling
Sefton Wonder	"	Russet Great Scot
Sharpe's Express	"	White Heather
Witchill	"	Snowdrop

Manual potato grader, early 1900's

Weighing machine, 1920's

another person's efforts and costs by offering high grade seed for sale.

New potato varieties continue to be introduced at a very quick rate. Many fall by the wayside and never reach the shops or gardener. A few acres are grown for a number of years then faults develop or they are discarded for superior varieties.

More eelworm resistant varieties are being introduced to the market which is beneficial to the gardener. Many new varieties are superior to some older varieties with more resistance to diseases and they produce higher yields. Very few floury textured varieties are appearing on the National List of new introductions. Of the few that have appeared most have been discarded very quickly. High yielding waxy varieties are the potato of today.

The Absence of Orders from the South

A feature of the Scottish potato trade in 1937 was the fact that demand was almost entirely restricted to local requirements. This fact was born out by the Potato Marketing Board in their report on the month's trade to 30th November, 1937, and they state that absence of orders from the south continued. While the Board had explained the reason for this continued absence of southern orders, it was understood that there were two premier reasons governing the position. In the first place it was due to heavy loadings in Lincolnshire and the second was cheaper quotations from Northern Ireland.

A good proportion of Irish potatoes were on offer in England. The 1937 season didn't produce much ware in Scotland and the prices on offer in the south hardly levelled up matters as far as the north was concerned when carriage was taken into account.

The Board in their report for the month's trading to 31st December, 1937 stated that business on the growers' market had been variable. The demand for white varieties had not come up to expectations, in spite of the fact that the colder weather had a good influence on consumption.

Later reports recorded that in the face of an apparently slow demand the tonnage leaving the main producing areas appeared to be substantial by early January (1938). There were more enquiries for supplies than of late and the tone of the markets was correspondingly cheerful. Prices showed little fluctuation but Warpland Majestics finished 2/6d per ton dearer at 80/-. King Edwards remained in strong demand and holders of outstanding samples commanded a price well in excess of the average for the season.

Change of Seed Location

It is well known that a change of seed from high lying districts to the lower lying areas of Scotland, England and Wales usually produces heavier crops. In favourable weather early varieties can be planted from late February onwards and maincrop varieties from April to early May (earlier in the south, later in the north). Earlier varieties should be given 24" between the rows and the tubers

12" to 14" apart in the rows. Maincrop varieties being stronger in the haulm, require 28" to 30" between the rows and 15" apart in the rows. A depth of 4" to 5" is considered correct for planting, depending on the size of the seed. Six kgs. of seed potatoes usually plants a row of about 60 ft.

Expansion of Potato Growing in Europe

It was approximately the early eighteenth century before potatoes were grown in quantity and introduced to commercial field culture. Prior to this time, potatoes were only cultivated in the gardens of Britain and continental Europe. By this date the potato had adapted to the long European growing days and climate.

With increased yields, this offered considerable potential to commercial growers such as farmers. Around the mid-1700's potatoes were widely grown in the North West of England. Such were the yields in the North West towards the end of the eighteenth century, that potatoes were exported to northern parts of Ireland and Dublin.

In and around London potatoes were becoming more accessible to the middle classes. Trading began in the London vegetable markets around 1750 - 1780, with locally grown potatoes from surrounding market growers. But the volume of potatoes grown at this time was small compared with the present day. In many parts of North East England and in Scotland potatoes were only being introduced to field culture at that time.

Irrigation

Extensive tests show that irrigation is beneficial to the potato crop, produces higher yields, reduces common scab, growth cracks and improves tuber quality but much depends on timing of irrigation. Very little benefit will be obtained by applying water at the wrong time or allowing the soil to become too dry. Before commencing irrigation growth cracking is usually associated with interuption of growth caused by drought followed by a period of rapid growth as a result of rain or late timed irrigation. The effect of irrigation on a ware crop can increase the yield by as much as 40% in a dry season.

Non irrigated crop

Irrigated crop ·

Chapter VII

The History of the Potato

The potato originated in South America and there is evidence of its cultivation and domestic use in Peru. By 3000 BC, records show that potatoes were grown for food in South America long before they were introduced to Europe. They first came to Spain in the early sixteenth century, and soon found their way into Ireland about the beginning of the eighteenth century where they became the staple diet. The story that Sir Walter Raleigh brought the potato to England from Virginia cannot be certain, as there are no records that potatoes were grown in Virginia at that time. Records show that potatoes were grown commercially in England towards the mid eighteenth century.

In France, the potato was privately cultivated and eaten on a small scale until the pharmacist, Antone-Auguste Parmentiar, recommended the potato as a solution to the country's widespread and recurring famine. There is an amusing story that shows Parmentier as something of an exponent of lateral thought. Early in the 1770's, Parmentier is said to have persuaded Louis the XV1 to let him plant a field of potatoes near Paris so as to spread the idea for the commercial growing of potatoes in France. Today the potato is firmly established as the third most important crop in the world.

The potato was the first cultivated crop not grown from seed and which matures underground as potatoes are grown from tubers. The arrival date of the potato into Britain remains a mystery. However, many leading authorities claim that the date of introduction was during the late 1500's. The potato was not readily accepted in Britain until it was fully acclimatised and was able to produce reasonable yields.

THE POTATO BONANZA
1882-1912

When the Colorado Beetle devastated the American Potato crop in 1882, huge quantities of potatoes were exported from Scotland to America, with Dundee as one of the main loading ports for transatlantic shipments. The potato boom lasted for thirty years from 1882 until 1912. With business reaching its peak in the first and last years. Farmers from all over the country rushed to share in the bonanza.

The liner companies to New York were overwhelmed with offers of cargo. Extra ships of all kinds were chartered. The demand for the potatoes in America was so great that it attracted several liner companies to the Dundee - New York trade. At one stage the Furness, Wilson Arrow and Atlantic Transport lines were operating competitive services, with exporters getting the benefit of cut price rates. Other ships involved were the Clan liners "Macbride" and "Macmillan" with other ships such as the "Messina" sailing for the Furness line. The Dundee whaler, "Arctic", the largest of the local fleet took a cargo of potatoes to St Johns, Newfoundland, before going to the spring sealing. Potatoes were not the only scarce vegetable on the other side of the Atlantic. Some ships loaded with part cargoes of turnips and part potatoes. Some of the chartered ships were not suitable for the winter crossings of the North Atlantic.

There were several cases of unscheduled calls at intermediate ports with engine trouble or for bunkering. One steamer, the "Mark Lane", spent 22 days grinding through an icefield off Newfoundland. Wooden fittings had to be burned to get her into Halifax (Nova Scotia) for bunkering. When she reached Philadelphia, the health authorities condemned 1800 tons of her 2000 ton cargo. A team of 33 dockers was engaged to dump the unfit potatoes at sea.

In the late 1800's potato exports from Dundee were running at the rate of 40,000 tons a year. Burntisland and Montrose, not normally loading ports for transatlantic cargoes shared in the traffic with smaller ships such as coasters ferrying potatoes from the smaller ports to Dundee for transatlantic shipments. Mussel dredgers at Tayport, over the Tay from Dundee stopped dredging from time to time and used their boats to take potatoes from Fife to Dundee for loading onto American bound ships.

Due to the shortage of cargo ships, potatoes were carried in the holds of passenger liners, with large quantities being sent by rail and small ships to English ports for transhipment. In the last year of the potato bonanza the liner "Titanic" was involved with potato cargo. Two hundred tons of Scottish grown Majestic seed potatoes from Angus was on board (in the hull), bound for the New York market on her ill-fated maiden voyage. The potatoes were exported by G. D. Maxwell, potato merchants and exporters, Montrose and Forfar (Scotland).

Good and bad years preceded the great and final boom of 1912, when the value of the potato exports to America reached $1,440,000. At one time in March of that year four steamers at Eastern Wharf, Dundee, were loading 10,000 tons of potatoes for the American market between them, which was a large tonnage in those days. In the boom years there were several cargoes in the 3,500 - 4,000 ton range and one of 4,600 tons loaded on to the "Messina" sailing for the Furness Line. All good things are inclined to come to an end and in the case of the transatlantic potato trade, the end was sudden and complete. Not a single potato was shipped in 1913 and the potato trade was lean for years after.

POTATO SHIPMENTS FROM EAST COAST PORTS

Potatoes have been extensively grown on the East Coast of Scotland, especially on the highly fertile soils of Angus, Perth, Fife and the Mearns since the mid-1800's with much of the potatoes being sold to England and Continental Europe. In the late 1800's until the 1930's potatoes were shipped from ports such as Montrose, Dundee, Arbroath, Burntisland, Dunbar and Leith to ports in the East of England such as the big seed centres round the Wash - King's Lynn, Boston and

Left :
Dressing seed potatoes, Thai
style, at a grading station near
Chiang Mai

Right:
Inspecting a Colorado Beetle
infected crop, Moscow region,
Russia. Mr Petrie of Angus
Fertilizers holding the plant.

Left:
Potato harvesting in Poland

Above and Right :
Potato pickers in Egypt

Below :
Harvesting a potato crop

Above : Packing potatoes in the field, Saudi Arabia

Below : High tec grading plant, Saudi Arabia

Left :
Grading in Israel

Below :
The plant on the right shows the benefits of new advanced plant food developments.
(Note leaves have been removed)

Left :
Gathering a potato crop in Cyprus

Left :
Gordon Smillie of Caithness Potatoes inspecting a potato crop grown from Scottish supplied seed

Below :
Potato digging by hand

Left :
Grading and prepacking potatoes

Left :
Harvesting in Denmark

Below :
Windrowing, Denmark

Below :
Harvesting, Holland

Above & Left :
Harvesting, Switzerland

Right :
Soil Preparation, Estonia

Left :
Potato grading

Below :
Potato harvesting

Above :
Harvesting, Jersey

Below :
Wet harvesting conditions in Southern Ireland, 1990

Above :
Planting trial plots in Tayside

Below :
Potato seedlings

Above :
Raising potato seedlings, Scotland

Below :
Potatoes growing for exhibition

Above :
A healthy potato crop, Angus, Scotland

Right :
Tuber tests, Scotland

Above :
American agronomist, Gerry Stoller (with the cap) discusses
nutrition of the potato crop with former SAC potato specialist
Simon Bowrn on his left on Carlungie Farm, Angus

Below :
Harvesting, Tayside

From left to right:

Marcel Guindi,
David Veitch,
Gordon Smilie,
Dr Jack Dunnett,
Bob Doig of Caithness
Potatoes

Left :
Charles Maisey at the
UK Championships
1993, Ebbn Vale, Wales

Varieties :
White Seedling,
Purple Eyed Seedling,
Sherine,
Bishop,
Kestrel

Above :
RHS Halls London
Collection of Six
Winner, Charles Maisey

Left : Potatoes on display at the Glasgow Festival 1988

Below : Winners 3 dish class, RHS Halls 1991 Varieties, Croft, Kestrel & Penta

Above : First Prize & The William Sands Memorial Trophy for Nadine and Maxine awarded to Claude Peace in the Scottish Branch Championship of the National Vegetable Society

Right : World Record for number of varieties exhibited (407). Private Collection by John Webster at Ayr, Scotland 1996

Sprouting can lead to blanks

Leafroll virus

Blight infected plants

Potash deficiency symptoms

Gangrene

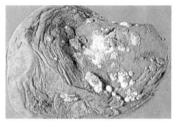

Dry Rot

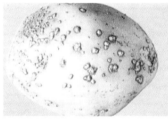

Skin Spot

Black Scurf

Silver Scurf

Potatoes arriving at Montrose Docks, Scotland for shipment 1970's

Wisbech and others like London, Hull and Weymouth.

Most of the potatoes were transported by coastal steamers such as the Montrose registered ships, the "Charlus", the "Belford", the "Port Leven", the "Slateford" and the ill-fated "Clint" which loaded a cargo of potatoes at Montrose bound for a south Channel port and foundered off Montrose on the 16th of March 1927 (all of her crew were saved). The "Clint" had carried many potato shipments from Montrose in previous years to ports on the East Coast of England.

Two of the Montrose steamers, the "Charlus" and the "Port Leven" were involved in the Dunkirk evacuations, happening to be in England at that time. Larger ships also loaded potatoes at Montrose for England, Continental Europe and the Middle East. Montrose docks were busy from time to time in the 1920's and 1930's with potato loadings.

Due to shortage of berthing space, it was common practice for ships to be berthed side by side. Strong battens were positioned across the inner ships to enable the dockers to load the outer ones. Until the 1940's, potatoes were transported from the local farms by horse drawn carts and from the distant farms by rail to the dockside.

TAYSIDE POTATOES WERE SEIZED AT SEA

Though the English market is the backbone of the potato trade in Scotland, the overseas side of the business has always been interesting to the Scottish growers and exporters. Spain had been a good customer for many years and there was usually an early cargo to Barcelona with other ships loading for the Balearic and Canary Islands. But during the Spanish Civil War a cargo of potatoes loaded part at Montrose and part at Dundee for Valencia, then in Government hands, was seized at sea by the Insurgents. The ship, the Norwegian "Lisken" was escorted to Vigo which belonged to the Franco side and the 1000 ton cargo was compulsorily unloaded.

MONEY PROBLEMS HOLD UP EXPORT OF SEED POTATOES

In November 1937, money difficulties held up thousands of pounds worth of Scottish seed potatoes for south Spain. For years this business had been an important feature of the potato industry in Angus, Perth and Fife.

The potatoes were normally shipped from Montrose and Dundee docks to Valencia and Malaga with resultant crops coming back to the U.K. the following summer as early potatoes. The Spanish buyers came over to Scotland making the usual contracts for big tonnage for early shipments. The first cargoes were already on the way to Spain when the question of finance arose. Pending agreement no further potatoes were loaded. It was of the utmost importance to the Scottish Potato Industry generally that the snag should be cleared and the bulk of the potatoes shipped out of the country.

The potato trade, both seed and ware, was none too good at that time and with thou-

Tattie squads from Dunkenny, Near Glamis, (top) and Ferryden, Scotland around 1906.

sands of tons booked for Spain thrown back on the market, the position became very uncomfortable for potato growers. In normal seasons England cleared a large percentage of the Scottish potato crop but in 1937 there was practically no buying with cheap quotations from Ireland. Prices were as low as 50/- per ton for top class table Majestics. How-ever, growers showed no inclination to part with their stocks at figures like these as they did not have to accept anything under 60/-, as the Potato Marketing Board would take their potatoes off their hands at 60/- per ton.

POTATO GROWING IN AYRSHIRE SCOTLAND

Since the 1800's, early potatoes have been widely grown in Ayrshire and famed for their good quality and new potato taste. In no other corner of Britain have farmers and potato growers developed more skill in the growing and production of early potatoes than the growers in Ayrshire.

Most of the seed planted was purchased in the north, mainly from the seed growing county of Angus. Many farmers planted the new seed on the inland fields for the first year to increase planting stocks and to get the new stock acclimatised to the new cli-

Ayrshire potato auctions, early 1900's

Potato growing in Ayrshire

mate, before being planted in the second year, to produce really early crops. There crops were generously treated with large amounts of farmyard manure and artificial fertilisers. Most of the early potato growing was concentrated on the coastline farms with much activity in the Girvan district of South Ayrshire. many potato merchants and buyers gathered in the country town of Girvan in the first half of the 1900's for auction sales. Fields were then visited and potato crops were sold by the acre as grown. To measure the average tonnage, a plant was dug and a tuber count taken, which was a guide to the amount of tons one acre would yield. It seems anomalous that crops grown with such skilful husbandry were still being dug by hand labour with the graip.

Ayrshire potato pickers, early 1900's

As late as the 1950's, most Ayrshire harvesting was done by large Irish contracting squads with agreed terms per acre or tonnage. There was usually a hitch between contracting squads and potato merchants regarding terms and their return fare home at the end of the engagement. In the early days seed was planted by hand. Then in the 1930's planting was done by a triplex driller drawn by two horses. By the year of 1938, for the first time all the weeding was undertaken by machine. Up until the 1940's potatoes were still gathered into wicker baskets, then into lightweight potato barrels on the field, then transported by horse drawn cart to the nearest railway station. They would then go by rail direct to the markets and shops of Glasgow and other large consuming centres.

Newly dug potatoes kept fresh much longer in barrels with less damage to the tubers than in sacks. Ayrshire was one of the last parts of Britain to use barrels for potatoes. At the start of the season yields would start as low as 3-4 tons per acre, increasing to 7-8 tons as the crop matured. The variety most widely grown was Epicure which monopolised the early crops until the late 1980's, being replaced with the modern high yielding varieties of today. Consumers of epicurean taste in potato quality may decry the Epicure variety. Such criticism has been common for many years, but it would be safe to say that Epicure's remarkable recovery power from late spring frost will be difficult to match by the modern varieties of today.

Horse drawn potato diggers, pre 1950's

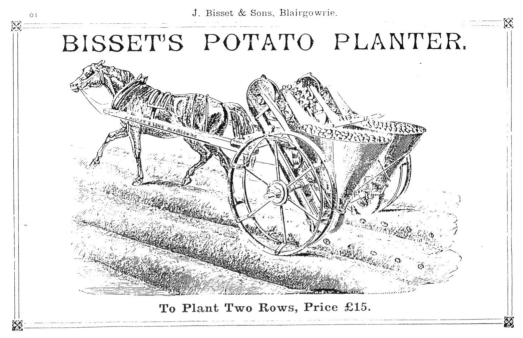

First potato planter, around 1867

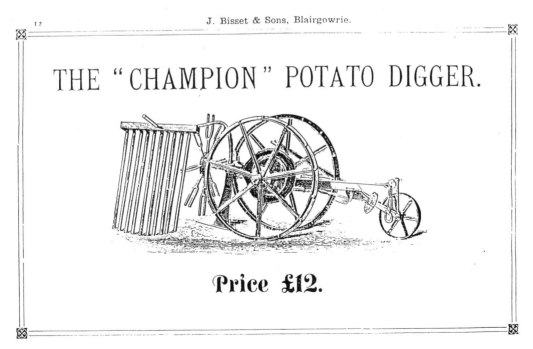

Potato digger from around 1890's

THE HISTORY OF EDZELL BLUE

The potato variety, Edzell Blue, was a sport found in a garden in the village of Edzell in Angus, Scotland during the late 1800's but was not introduced to the market until 1915. The true Edzell Blue has very rough dark blue skin and pure white floury flesh with blue veins and deep eyes.

Edzell Blues have been very popular as a garden variety in Scotland since its introduction, especially for its culinary qualities. Local farmer Mr David Arnot of Mains of Edzell Farm cultivated and perfected the variety after long experiments and cross-pollination. Mr Arnot then sold 60 Edzell Blue tubers to a South African potato farmer at the colossal price of £1 per tuber in 1918. The potatoes were wrapped in cotton wool then in small squares of corrugated paper. Each carefully wrapped tuber was placed into individual sections of specially made wooden trays, and finally each item was wedged with cylinders of more corrugated paper in each corner. The potatoes were then exported to South Africa by an Aberdeen seed firm.

The village Edzell, home of the Edzell Blues

Chapter VIII

Potato Varieties of Today

Accent (1989)
A round oval white variety maturing as a first early. Eyes are shallow. Flesh is pale yellow and of firm waxy texture. Matures slightly earlier than Home Guard. Cooking qualities are good. Produces a high yield of medium sized tubers. Susceptible to virus X. Resistant to potato cyst nematode (R.O. pathotype). Foliage is of medium height.

Adora (1989)
An oval white variety maturing as a first early. Tubers are shallow-eyed, flesh is cream and of semi-waxy texture, has excellent cooking qualities, with good resistance to after-cooking discolouration. Also has good resistance to powdery scab, blackleg, common scab and drought.

Agri (1989)
A long oval, white variety maturing as an early maincrop. Produces a very high yield of large uniform tubers with shallow eyes and yellow flesh of semi-floury texture. A suitable variety for processing, chipping and as a boiled potato. Has high resistance to virus Y and A. Has moderate resistance to leafroll, good resistance to phytophthora both in foliage and tubers. Resistant to potato cyst nematode pathotype (R.O.I.+4A).

Atlantic (1991)
A round, white variety maturing as an early maincrop, produces a high yield of good sized white fleshed tubers with semi-floury texture. Eyes are of medium depth. Recommended for baking, boiling, and roasting.

Has good resistance to common scab and most potato diseases. An eelworm resistant variety.

Amadeus (1995)
A round to oval red variety, maturing as an early maincrop, produces a high yield of good sized tubers with very little waste. Eyes are shallow, flesh is yellow of waxy texture. All round cooking qualities are good. Has very good resistance to blight with some resistance to most other diseases. Resistant to potato cyst nematode (R.O. pathotype).

Ailsa (1984) *above*
A round white variety maturing as an early maincrop. Produces a high yield of nicely shaped tubers with cream flesh, semi-waxy texture and shallow eyes. Recommended for boiling, baking, chipping and roasting. Highly resistant to blackleg and external damage, making Ailsa a good variety for

winter storing. Rather susceptible to tuber and foliage blight. Susceptible to spraing and virus Y. Very acceptable to a range of climates and conditions. Foliage is low and bushy. Ailsa is suitable for growing in open windy areas.

Alcmaria (1969) *above*

A long oval white variety, maturing as a first early, produces a good yield of bold tubers with shallow eyes. Flesh is yellow and of waxy texture. Cooking qualities are good. Tubers tending to coarseness when fully matured, susceptible to rhizoctonia. Resistant to cyst nematode (R.O. pathotype) with some resistance to common scab and slug damage. Foliage is of medium height.

Aminca (1977)

A long oval white variety maturing as a first early. Produces a good yield of good sized tubers with cream flesh of waxy texture and shallow eyes. Cooking qualities are good and reasonably free from disintegration and discolouration. Has moderate resistance to tuber blight, gangrene, common scab, leafroll and spraing. Susceptible to foliage blight, resistant to cyst nematode (R.O. pathotype).

Arkula (1982)

An oval white variety maturing as a first early. Produces a good yield of good sized tubers. Eyes are shallow, flesh is of firm waxy texture. Excellent for jacket potatoes and chipping. Has good resistance to spraing. Susceptible to foliage and tuber blight, also blackleg. Foliage is of medium height and spreading.

Arran Banner (1927)

A round white variety maturing as an early maincrop. Produces a heavy yield of large tubers with white flesh and firm moist texture which does not discolour after cooking. Eyes are medium to deep. Has good resistance to drought and dry rot, with some resistance to blight, gangrene and common scab. Very popular with English gardeners.

Arran Comet (1956)

An oval white variety maturing as a first early. Produces a high yield of medium sized tubers with shallow eyes. Flesh is cream and of waxy texture. An excellent variety for early scraping, does not disintegrate on cooking. Good for boiling and salad use. Has good resistance to after-cooking discolouration, gangrene, bruising, common scab and drought.

Arran Consul (1925)

An oval white variety maturing as an early maincrop. Produces a moderate yield of good sized tubers with deep eyes. Flesh is light cream and of floury texture with exceptional table quality. Has a tendency to blacken after cooking. Rarely sprouts in storage. Tubers are best set out in trays in warm conditions early in the Spring to give them an early start. Resistant to gangrene, susceptible to blight, drought and leafroll virus. Foliage is of medium height.

Arran Pilot (1930)

An oval white variety maturing as a first early. Produces a heavy crop of good sized tubers with medium to shallow eyes. Flesh is white and of waxy texture. Has good resistance to common scab, drought and spraing. Susceptible to blackleg.

Arran Victory (1918)

A round oval blue variety maturing as a late maincrop. Produces a heavy crop that keeps well through the winter. Flesh is pure white and of floury texture with excellent cooking qualities, especially as a boiled jacket or chipping potato. Has a real potato taste. Foliage is tall, vigorous and upright. Resistant to common scab (one of the best blues).

Avalanche (1989)

A long oval white variety maturing as an early maincrop. Produces a good yield of smooth skinned nicely shaped tubers with shallow eyes. Flesh is white and of firm texture and excellent cooking qualities with good resistance to after-cooking discolouration. Has good resistance to dry rot, common scab, gangrene and bruising. Foliage is of medium height and upright growth.

Avondale (1982)

A round oval white variety, maturing as a late maincrop. Fleish is cream, of firm waxy texture, eyes are of medium depth. Has high resistance to blackleg, bruising, common scab, dry rot and after-cooking discolouration. Avondale is ideal for baking and boiling.

Ausonia (1983) *above*

A round oval white variety maturing as a second early. Produces a moderate crop of medium to large sized tubers of semi-floury texture. Flesh is light yellow. Eyes are shallow to medium. All round cooking qualities are good, especially as a baker. Flesh is free from after-cooking discolouration. Susceptible to powdery scab and gangrene. Resistant to cyst nematode (R.O. pathotype).

Baillie (1981) *above*

A round oval white variety maturing as a second early. Tubers are nicely shaped with shallow eyes. Flesh is cream and of firm waxy texture with good cooking qualities and good flavour. Moderately resistant to dry rot, blight, and common scab. Susceptible to gangrene, moderately resistant to virus Y.

Ballydoon (1931)

An oval white variety maturing as a first early. Flesh is white and of firm texture. Eyes are of medium depth. Cooking qualities are good. This variety is not widely grown, but can still be found in specialist catalogues. Foliage is of medium height to tall.

Balmoral (1989)

A beautiful pink-eyed long oval variety maturing as a second early. The cooking quality of Balmoral is exceptional with creamy flesh, firm waxy texture and shallow eyes. Suitable for boiling, baking and chipping. Produces a good yield of good sized tubers with a fine skin finish, making Balmoral a good show variety. Has some resistance to blight, drought and powdery scab.

Belle De Fontenay (1885)

A long yellow skinned variety maturing as a second early. Produces a moderate yield of small kidney shaped tubers with shallow eyes. Flesh is yellow and of waxy texture with fine taste, an excellent variety for salad use. Susceptible to blight, virus infection and crop failure in dry conditions. Foliage is low and spreading.

Berber (1985)

A long oval white variety maturing as a first early, produces a high yield of large tubers with shallow to medium eyes. Flesh is pale yellow and of firm waxy texture with good all round cooking qualities, and free from after-cooking discolouration. Has good resistance to external damage and virus Y and moderate resistance to gangrene, common scab, spraing, leafroll virus and tuber blight. Resistant to potato cyst nematode (R.O. pathotype).

Bintje (1910)

An oval yellow skinned variety maturing as an early maincrop. Eyes are shallow, flesh is a light yellow and of semi-floury waxy texture. Cooking qualities are good, but has a slight tendency to after-cooking discolouration and disintegration. Recommended for French fries. Has some resistance to most common potato diseases. Foliage is of medium height and spreading (produces a good yield).

Bonte Desiree (1976)

A long oval white to red variety, maturing as an early maincrop. Produces a moderate yield of bold tubers with light yellow flesh of waxy texture and shallow eyes with good all round cooking qualities. Rarely discolours after cooking. Has good resistance to drought and powdery scab. Foliage is of medium height and spreading.

Bright (1988)

A round, oval, white variety maturing as an early maincrop, produces a good yield of good sized tubers with superficial eyes. Flesh is white and of dry texture which remains firm when boiled, with good all round cooking qualities. Has good resistance to foliage and tuber blight. Highly resistant to viruses. Susceptible to cyst nematode (R.O. pathotype). Good resistance to drought and highly suitable for organic production.

Blanka (1970)

A long, oval, white variety maturing as a second early. Produces a high yield of medium sized tubers with superficial eyes. Flesh is pure white and of dry texture that remains firm when boiled. Has moderate resistance to after-cooking discolouration. Moderate resistance to foliage blight and leafroll virus with low resistance to gangrene and common scab. Immune to wart disease but not to cyst namatode (R.O. pathotype). Good resistance to drought.

British Queen (1894)
An oval white variety maturing as a second early. Produces a reasonable yield of medium sized tubers of floury texture. Boils to mash when over-cooked, has real old fashioned potato taste. Has good resistance to slug damage, susceptible to blight and wart disease. Foliage is of medium height.

Brodick (1990)
A long oval white pink eyed variety maturing as an early maincrop. Has good cooking qualities. Brodick is excellent for boiling, baking and jacket potatoes. Tubers are shallow eyed with cream flesh and of firm waxy texture. Keeps well in storage through the winter. Has good resistance to foliage blight, gangrene and virus Y. Prone to after-cooking discolouration.

Brodie (1993)
A long oval pink-eyed variety maturing as an early maincrop. Produces a good yield of nicely shaped tubers with shallow eyes. Flesh is cream and of waxy texture suitable for table use, with good baking content. Has good resistance to drought and blackleg.

Cara (1976)
A beautifully round-oval pink-eyed variety, maturing as a late maincrop. Produces a very high yield of large tubers with shallow eyes, flesh is cream and of firm semi-floury/waxy texture which remains firm when cooked. A top class baking potato having good all round cooking qualities, with good resistance to after-cooking discoloura-

tion. High resistance to foliage and tuber blight, common scab, bruising and is eelworm resistant. Very susceptible to powdery scab and slug damage. Foliage is tall.

Carlingford (1982)
A round oval white variety maturing as a second early. Tubers are of medium size with shallow eyes, flesh is white with a pale lemon tinge and of waxy texture with good flavour. Free from after cooking blackening, an excellent variety for boiling, roasting and salads. Has some resistance to drought, blackleg, skin spot and powdery scab. Foliage is of medium height. An excellent variety for double cropping out of season new potatoes.

Catriona (1920)
A long purple-eyed variety maturing as a second early. Flesh is a soft white with a lemon tinge and floury texture. Eyes are shallow. Catriona has excellent cooking qualities and good flavour, a top show variety when well grown. Has some resistance to most diseases. Susceptible to dry rot and hollow heart.

Charlotte (1981)
A long oval white variety maturing as a second early. Tubers are shallow eyed, flesh is a creamy yellow of firm waxy texture with excellent cooking qualities. Good for potato salads, resistant to after cooking discolouration (blackening). Susceptible to cyst eelworm.

Cleopatra (1981)
A long oval red variety maturing as a first early. Eye depth is medium, flesh is pale yellow and of firm waxy texture. Produces a good yield of nicely shaped tubers. Cooking qualities are good and is relatively free from

after-cooking blackening. Has good resistance to dry rot, skin spot, common scab and bruising but susceptible to eelworm.

Colleen (1993)
A round oval creamy yellow-skinned variety, maturing as a first early. Flesh is light yellow and of semi-dry texture, eyes are of medium depth. Produces a high yield. Has good resistance to bruising, drought, blight and after-cooking discolouration. A multi-purpose first early variety.

Colmo (1979)
An oval white variety maturing as a first early. Has shallow eyes with yellow flesh of waxy texture. Cooking qualities are good, especially as a mashed and baking potato. Has some resistance to most common diseases. Foliage is of medium height and spreading. Produces a good yield of large tubers.

Concorde (1988) *below*
A long oval white variety maturing as a first early with shallow eyes. Flesh is pale yellow and of firm waxy texture with good taste. Cooking qualities are reasonably good. Resistant to golden eelworm and virus Y. Has some resistance to most diseases.

Concurrent (1991)
A round oval white variety maturing as a first early. Produces a heavy crop of good sized tubers of good cooking and eating quality. Tubers are of firm waxy texture, cream flesh and shallow eyes. Free from both disintegration and after-cooking discolouration. Has good resistance to blight, common scab and drought. Susceptible to leafroll virus, virus Y and cyst nematode. Foliage is of medium height.

Corine (1976)
A round oval white variety maturing as a first early. Eyes are shallow to medium, flesh is light yellow and of firm texture. Produces a high yield of good sized tubers, cooking qualities are good. Foliage is of low to medium height and spreading. Has some all round resistance to most diseases found in the garden.

Costella (1984)
A round oval white variety maturing as a second early. Produces a heavy crop of good sized tubers with shallow eyes. Yellow flesh of waxy texture. Cooking qualities are excellent, a good all-round favourite with good baking content. Has good resistance to blight, common scab and cyst nematode. Foliage is of medium height and vigorous.

Craigs Alliance (1948)
An oval white variety maturing as a first early. Produces a moderate yield of uniform tubers with white flesh of waxy texture. Has good all round cooking qualities with good resistance to after-cooking discolouration. Eyes are shallow. Foliage is of medium height and bushy. Susceptible to drought. (Good for exhibition).

Cultra (1988)

An oval white part-red variety maturing as an early maincrop. Produces a good yield of nicely shaped tubers with shallow to medium eyes. Flesh is cream and semi-floury/waxy texture, with nice flavour and good all round cooking qualities. Has good resistance to after-cooking discolouration. Fairly good resistance to blight, common scab, gangrene, blackleg, dry rot and powdery scab. Resistant to potato cyst nematode. (Good for exhibition).

Desiree (1962)

A long oval red variety maturing as an early maincrop. Produces a high yield of good sized tubers of waxy texture. Flesh is pale yellow. An excellent variety for boiling and baking, rarely discolours after cooking. Has good resistance to drought, gangrene, dry rot, powdery scab and bruising.

Diamant (1982)

A long oval white variety maturing as an early maincrop. Eyes are shallow. Flesh is light yellow and of waxy texture. All round cooking qualities are good with a high baking content. Has good resistance to most diseases found in the garden (especially blight). Foliage is of medium height.

Diana (1982)

A round oval red variety maturing as an early maincrop. Produces a large yield of large uniform tubers with shallow eyes. Flesh is cream and of firm waxy texture. Diana has excellent cooking qualities with high resistance to after-cooking blackening. Moderately susceptible to foliage blight, virus Y and leafroll virus. Foliage is of medium height. A good variety for exhibition.

Di Vernon (1922)

A long white part-coloured variety maturing as a first early. Produces a high yield of nicely shaped tubers with shallow eyes. Flesh is light yellow and of floury texture with good all round cooking qualities. Has good resistance to after-cooking discolouration, and a very pleasing flavour. Has good resistance to common scab, drought and skin spot. Foliage is low to medium height.

Doon Star (1926)

An oval white variety maturing as an early maincrop. Produces a moderate yield of good-sized tubers with shallow eyes. Flesh is cream and of waxy texture with good cooking qualities especially for roasting. Has a real potato taste and some resistance to most potato diseases. Foliage is of medium height and vigorous.

Duke of York (1891)

An oval white variety maturing as a first early. Produces a moderate yield of medium sized tubers with shallow eyes and yellow floury flesh which remains firm when cooked. Has a real potato flavour with good all round cooking qualities, especially for baking and chipping. Susceptible to blight. A very popular variety in Scotland.

Dunbar Rover (1936)

A round oval white variety maturing as a second early. Produces a huge crop of large tubers with shallow eyes and white flesh of floury texture. An excellent variety for boiling, baking and chipping. Has some resistance to most potato diseases. A suitable variety for light soils. Foliage is of medium height.

Dunbar Standard (1936)

A long oval white variety maturing as a late maincrop with floury texture, cream flesh and shallow eyes. Has excellent cooking qualities (recommended for chipping). Produces a huge crop. Keeps well in storage during the winter. Has a tendency to blacken after cooking. Has some resistance to most potato diseases. Foliage is of medium height.

Dundrum (1983)

A round oval white variety maturing as a second early. Produces a good yield of even sized tubers with light cream flesh and of waxy texture. Eyes are shallow to medium depth. All round cooking qualities are good, has some resistance to most diseases found in the garden. Foliage is of medium height.

Dundrod (1987)

An oval white variety maturing as a first early. Produces a moderate yield of good sized tubers with cream flesh of waxy texture. Eyes are shallow to moderately deep. Cooking qualities are reasonably good. Has good resistance to virus Y and skin spot, fairly susceptible to tuber blight and leafroll virus. Resistant to potato cyst nematode (R.O. pathotype). Foliage is of medium height.

Dunluce (1976)

An oval white variety maturing as a first early with firm waxy texture, cream flesh and shallow eyes. Ideal for boiling and salads. An excellent variety for forcing under glass. Susceptible to drought and blight.

Edzell Blue (1915)

A round blue variety maturing as a second early. Flesh is snow white and of floury texture. Eyes are medium to deep. This old variety is very much asked for but has been out of production for some years. Now reintroduced in small quantities. Has good resistance to drought, powdery scab and dry rot. Suscep-tible to blight.

Epicure (1897)

A round white skinned variety turning pink on exposure, maturing as a first early. Produces a good yield of smooth skinned tubers with deep eyes and raised eyebrows. Flesh is white and of semi-floury texture. Taste is superb with good cooking qualities. Withstands late frosts which makes Epicure very reliable with good resistance to most potato diseases.

Estima (1973)

A high quality variety maturing as a second early. Tubers are round oval with cream flesh, shallow eyes and slightly waxy texture. Estima is good for boiling and baking. Has a blemish free skin, and is free from discolouration and disintegration. Has good resistance to blight, slug damage and drought. Susceptible to blackleg, spraing, and virus Y (severe Mosaic). Keeps well in storage all through the winter.

Fambo (1986)

A long white variety maturing as a second early. Eyes are shallow, flesh is pale yellow and of waxy texture. Bulks early and stores well. Has excellent all round cooking qualities and is reasonably free from after-cooking blackening. Recommended for chipping. Has good resistance to gangrene, skin spot and common scab. Has low resistance to drought, blackleg and powdery scab.

Famosa (1977)

A long oval white variety maturing as an early maincrop. Tubers are large, tending to be rather course and variable in shape. Produces a good yield and cooking qualities are quite good. Has resistance to blight. Susceptible to gangrene and virus diseases including virus Y to which it is highly tolerant.

Fianna (1988)

A long oval white variety maturing as an early maincrop. Tubers are nicely shaped with shallow eyes, flesh is white and of firm waxy texture. All round cooking qualities are excellent, but has a slight tendency towards after-cooking blackening. Has good resistance to foliage blight, blackleg, common and powdery scab and bruising.

Foremost (1954)

An oval white variety maturing as a first early. Produces a good crop of firm white fleshed tubers with shallow eyes. Has a real new potato taste. The cooking qualities of Foremost are excellent. Keeps well in storage. Has some resistance to gangrene, skin spot, dry rot and slug damage.

Foxton (1981)

An oval red variety maturing as an early maincrop. Produces a reasonable crop, eyes are of medium depth, flesh is a light yellow and of semi-floury texture. Cooking qualities are reasonably good. Has good resistance to dry rot, gangrene and skin spot. Moderately resistant to virus Y, but rather susceptible to common scab and leafroll virus. Foliage is of medium height.

Fresco (1985)

A long oval yellow-skinned variety maturing as a first early. Eyes are shallow. Flesh is light yellow and of waxy texture, with good all round cooking qualities. Has good resistance to tuber blight, common scab and drought. Resistant to potato cyst, nematode (R.O. pathotype).

Fronika (1985)

A round oval white variety maturing as a second early. Eyes are of medium depth. Flesh is light yellow and of semi-waxy texture. Produces a very high yield of good sized tubers of excellent quality. An excellent baking potato. Resistant to cyst nematode (R.O. pathotype) and has good resistance to common scab.

Glamis (1992)

A long, oval, pink-eyed variety, maturing as an early maincrop. Produces a high yield of good sized tubers of semi-floury texture with shallow eyes and pale cream flesh. Recommended for baking, boiling and roasting. Has good resistance to common scab and most other potato diseases, with good resistance to drought. Having a nice smooth skin finish makes Glamis an ideal exhibition variety. Susceptible to cyst eelworm.

Granola (1975)

A round, oval, white variety maturing as an early maincrop. Produces a high yield of large sized tubers with shallow to medium eyes. Flesh is pale yellow and of semi-floury texture. Cooking qualities are good, especially as a boiled or baked potato and is free from after-cooking discolouration. Has good resistance to most diseases including R.O.I. nematode.

Gracia (1979)

A round, oval, red variety maturing as a second early. Produces a medium yield of large tubers with shallow eyes and light yellow flesh of dry texture. Cooking qualities are good and free from after cooking discolouration. Has moderate resistance to potato diseases. None immune to cyst nematode. An excellent show variety when well grown.

Golden Wonder (1904)

A long oval russet variety maturing as a late maincrop. Flesh is white with a lemon tinge and floury texture. An excellent variety for baking, chipping and as a jacket potato. Careful boiling is necessary to prevent disintegration. Taste is superb. Well fertilised soil is required to grow this variety. Resistant to common scab with good resistance to blight, gangrene, skin spot, and dry rot. Foliage is tall, eyes are of medium depth.

Heather (1993)

A long oval purple variety maturing as a second early. Produces a good yield of good quality tubers with smooth skins and shallow eyes. Flesh is pure white and of waxy texture with good all round cooking qualities. Has moderate resistance to most potato diseases, and is eelworm resistant. Foliage is of medium height.

Home Guard (1942)

An oval white variety maturing as a first early. Produces a medium yield of good sized tubers with white flesh of firm waxy texture. Cooking quality is good but deteriorates on keeping. Sprouts early and rapid, requires moist growing conditions to yield well. Tubers are shallow-eyed and attractive, but are consequently prone to shrinkage. Has poor resistance to drought and frost recovery. Susceptible to blight and gangrene. A good variety for the organic gardener.

Jewel (1985)

A round oval white variety maturing as an early maincrop. Produces a heavy yield of large tubers of firm waxy texture with shallow eyes and cream flesh, which is free from after-cooking discol-ouration. Susceptible to gangrene and slug damage. Has moderate resistance to common scab, foliage blight and virus Y, resistant to cyst nematode (R.O. pathotype).

Junior (1990)

A long oval white variety maturing as a first early. Eyes are of medium depth. Flesh is a light yellow and of semi-floury waxy texture. Matures earlier than Home Guard. Has good all round cooking qualities. Susceptible to tuber blight and virus X. Resistant to potato cyst nematode. (R.O. pathotype).

Karlena (1993)

A round oval yellow-skinned variety, maturing as a first early. Flesh is pale yellow and of semi-floury texture. Eyes are of medium depth. An excellent variety for boiling and baking. Has good resistance to common scab, blackleg, bruising and after-cooking discolouration. Produces a high number of attractive tubers.

Kennebeck (1963)

An oval white variety maturing as an early maincrop. Produces a good yield of large tubers with eyes of medium depth. Flesh is cream and of waxy texture. Excellent for baking and boiling, is resistant to after-cooking discolouration. Has good resistance to foliage and tuber blight and common scab.

Kerr's Pink (1917)

A round pink variety, somewhat flat, dented at heel, maturing as a late maincrop. Produces a medium yield of good sized tubers with medium to deep eyes. Flesh is pure white and of floury texture with a real potato taste. A very vigorous grower. Foliage is of medium height to tall, has some resistance to most potato diseases. An excellent variety for over-winter storing.

Kestrel (1992)

A beautiful long blue-eyed variety maturing as a second early. The cooking quality of Kestrel is exceptional with a firm cream flesh, semi-waxy floury texture and shallow eyes. Suitable for boiling, baking and chipping. Produces a good yield of good sized tubers. Has a very fine skin finish, making Kestrel a top flight show potato. Featured in the U.K. Potato Championships in 1992-93 and the R.H.S. Exhibition, London, 1991. Has good resistance to slug damage and is eelworm resistant, with good resistance to most other diseases. A superb potato.

King Edward (1902)

A round oval white variety part pink. Characteristically smooth on surface. Eyes are shallow, flesh is cream and of floury texture. Has good all round cooking qualities. Foliage is of medium height. A popular variety and good for exhibition. Susceptible to blight, wart disease, drought and virus Y.

Kingston (1981)

An oval white variety maturing as a late maincrop. Produces a high yield of good sized tubers with white flesh of waxy texture and shallow eyes. Excellent for baking and boiling with a little tendency to blacken after cooking. Susceptible to skin spot, dry rot and slug damage. Moderately resistant to common scab. Resistant to cyst nematode (R.O. pathotype).

Kirsty (1982)

A round white variety maturing as an early maincrop. Eyes are shallow. Flesh is a soft creamy white and of semi-waxy texture an excellent variety for roast, jacket and baking. A vigorous grower with late foliage maturity. Has some resistance to blackleg. Susceptible to spraing and slug damage. Foliage is of medium height to tall.

Kondor (1984)

An oval red variety maturing as an early maincrop. Eyes are medium to deep. Tubers are large with cream flesh and of firm waxy texture, remains firm when boiled. Produces a high yield, has good resistance to blight. Foliage is vigorous and tall upright.

Lady Rosetta (1988)

A russet red variety maturing as an early maincrop. Tubers are shallow to medium eyed, flesh is pale yellow and of firm dry texture with good flavour. Has good resistance to foliage and tuber blight and after -cooking discolouration. Susceptible to dry rot, gangrene and skin spot.

Linzer Delikatess (1975)

A long oval white maturing as a second early. Produces a large crop of medium sized tubers of firm waxy texture with shallow eyes. Flesh is a soft yellow. Mostly grown for salad use. Susceptible to cyst eelworm. This variety requires lots of irrigation.

Liseta (1989)

A long oval white variety maturing as a second early. Produces a high yield of good sized tubers with yellow flesh of firm waxy texture which is free from after-cooking discolouration. Has good resistance to tuber blight, drought and common scab. Partially resistant to cyst nematode (R.O. pathotype). Susceptible to wart disease.

Lola (1981)

A long oval white variety maturing as a first early. Produces a good crop of evenly sized tubers with shallow eyes. Flesh is pale yellow and of waxy texture. Lola has good all-round cooking qualities and is free from after-cooking discolouration, with high resistance to common scab and virus Y. Susceptible to tuber blight. Foliage is of medium height.

Lutetia (1988)

An oval white variety maturing as a second early. A variety widely grown in Italy which could also suit the U.K. Tubers are nicely shaped, produces a good yield of good quality potatoes with cream flesh of firm waxy texture and shallow eyes. Stores well and has good resistance to most potato diseases.

Majestic (1911)

A long oval white variety maturing as an early maincrop. Tubers are pear shaped, eyes are of medium depth. Flesh is white and of waxy texture with good cooking qualities. Has a slight tendency to discolour after cooking. Produces a huge crop. Large tubers can be prone to growth cracking when over mature. Keeps well in over-winter storage

and is drought resistant. Has good resistance to blight, dry rot and powdery scab. Foliage is of medium height.

Morag (1985)

A round white variety maturing as an early maincrop. Tubers are nicely shaped with white flesh of semi-waxy texture and shallow eyes. Excellent for boiling, baking, chipping and roasting. Has good resistance to leafroll virus, partially resistant to both golden and pale eelworm. Susceptible to virus Y and tuber blight. Good for exhibition. Foliage is low to medium height.

Manna (1977)

A long oval white variety maturing as a first early. Produces a heavy crop of shallow-eyed tubers of waxy texture. Cooking qualities are excellent, flesh is a light yellow. Susceptible to blight and blackleg, good for exhibition.

Marfona (1977) *above*

A round white variety maturing as a second early. Produces a huge crop of uniform tubers of firm waxy texture with pale yellow flesh and shallow eyes. Has good cooking qualities. Excellent for jacket potatoes.

Cooks well without discolouration. Marfona has good foliage cover which can be an asset on light soils for moisture retention.

Maris Bard (1972) *below*
A long oval white variety maturing as a first early. Tubers are shallow-eyed, flesh is white and of waxy texture. Produces a high yield of good sized tubers, sprouts relatively late, but matures very early. Good results can be obtained if forced under glass or polythene. Cooking qualities are good and free from after-cooking discolouration. Has good resistance to gangrene, dry rot, common scab, drought and bruising.

Maris Peer (1962)
A round oval white variety maturing as a second early. Has white waxy flesh and shallow eyes. Produces a moderate yield of small to medium sized tubers. An excellent variety for roast (and baby roasts), and as an early scraper. Has good resistance to both common and powdery scab, and skin spot, with moderate resistance to foliage and tuber blight. Susceptible to drought. An early sprouter.

Maris Piper (1963)
An oval white variety maturing as an early maincrop. One of the most popular varieties. Has excellent cooking qualities. A first class chipper. Flesh is creamy white and floury textured with good flavour. Rarely discolours on cooking. Tubers are shallow eyed. Resistant to gangrene and cyst nematode (R.O. pathotype). Susceptible to leafroll, slug damage, common and powdery scab with some resistance to blackleg.

Minerva (1988)
An oval white variety maturing as a first early. Eyes are of medium depth. Flesh is cream and of waxy texture. Has good all round cooking qualities and good resistance to internal bruising. Minerva is resistant to potato cyst nematode (R.O. pathotype). Foliage is of medium height to tall.

Monalisa (1982)
A long, oval, white variety maturing as a second early. Tubers are shallow-eyed with light yellow flesh of firm waxy texture. An excellent salad potato and a top show variety. Has good resistance to most diseases found in the garden. Foliage is of medium height.

Mondial (1989)
A long oval white variety maturing as an early maincrop, tubers are shallow to medium eyed. Flesh is pale yellow and of slightly mealy texture. Cooking qualities are good and rarely suffers from after-cooking discolouration. Has good resistance to blight, common scab, drought, blackleg and bruising, can suffer from gangrene and powdery scab.

Morene (1983)
A long oval white variety, maturing as an early maincrop. Eyes are shallow to medium

depth, flesh is a pale cream, soft and mealy with a slight tendency towards disintegration and after-cooking blackening. Cooking qualities are excellent (bakes well). Has good resistance to drought, common scab, bruising and blight.

Nadine (1987) *above*
A round oval white variety, maturing as a second early. Produces a large crop of good sized, uniform tubers with shallow eyes. Flesh is cream and of waxy texture which remains firm and moist on cooking with no after-cooking discolouration. Has good resistance to blight, common scab, gangrene, skin spot, powdery scab and bruising. Foliage is of medium height. A superb potato.

Navan (1987)
A round white variety maturing as an early maincrop. Has good cooking qualities, excellent for boiling, baking and chipping. Tubers are nicely shaped with shallow eyes and white flesh. Has good resistance to blackleg, blight and drought and is eelworm resistant.

Nicola (1973)
A long oval yellow skinned variety maturing as a second early. Produces a high yield of large tubers. Eyes are of medium depth, flesh is yellow and of waxy texture. An excellent variety for boiling or salad use. Has good resistance to most potato diseases. This is a popular variety in Continental Europe, but seldom been grown in the U.K. as seed was not readily available. Foliage is of medium height and slightly spreading.

Obelix (1988)
An oval white variety maturing as an early maincrop. Produces a high yield of large tubers with shallow eyes. Flesh is light yellow and of firm waxy texture, bulks early. A good baking variety, susceptible to tuber blight and virus Y. Resistant to leafroll, potato cyst nematode (R.O. pathotype). Moderately resistant to common scab.

Ostara (1980) *above*
An oval yellow-skinned variety maturing as a first early. Eyes are shallow, flesh is a light yellow and of waxy texture. Has reasonable all-round cooking qualities as an early pota-

to. Produces a good yield, bulks early, sprouts are red. Foliage is of medium height. Has good resistance to common scab and spraing. Susceptible to potato cyst eelworm.

Penta (1983) *below*
A beautiful round pink-eyed variety maturing as a second early. Has good cooking qualities with high marks for boiling, baking and chipping. Flesh is cream, eyes are medium to shallow. Produces a high yield of good sized tubers. Has good resistance to blight. Penta has scored high marks on the show bench since its introduction. Tubers are true round. Eelworm resistant.

Pentland Crown (1958)
An oval white variety maturing as an early maincrop with waxy white flesh and shallow eyes. Produces a huge crop of good sized tubers. Cooking qualities are moderate. Resistant to leafroll virus, common scab and virus Y. Susceptible to powdery scab and gangrene. Has good resistance to drought. An excellent variety for over winter storage.

Pentland Dell (1960)
A long, oval, white variety maturing as an early maincrop. Produces a high yield of good quality tubers with white flesh of semi-floury texture with good cooking qualities especially for baking, chipping and roasting, but has a slight tendency to blacken and to disintegrate on boiling. Liable to small potato, to prevent this use sprouted seed and avoid planting in cold soil. Has some resistance to skin spot and common scab. Susceptible to blight and spraing. Eyes are shallow.

Pentland Hawk (1967)
An oval white variety maturing as an early maincrop. Produces a moderate yield of good sized tubers with pale cream flesh of firm dry floury texture with good flavour; occasionally suffers from after-cooking blackening. A good variety for salads, boiling and chipping. Eyes are shallow, an excellent variety for long term storage. Has some resistance to blight, drought and gangrene. Susceptible to spraing and virus Y.

Pentland Ivory (1966)
A round, oval, white variety maturing as an early maincrop. Produces high yields of shapely tubers with shallow eyes and pale cream flesh of floury texture with good cooking qualities. Has some resistance to tuber blight and common scab. Resistant to virus Y. Susceptible to spraing. Foliage is of medium height.

Pentland Javelin (1968)
An oval white variety maturing as a first early. Tubers are nicely shaped with shallow eyes. Flesh is pure white and of firm waxy texture with good cooking qualities. Tends to be a very slow sprouter. Has good resistance to common scab and is resistant to cyst nematode (R.O. pathotype).

Pentland Lustre (1969)

A round oval part-coloured white maturing as a first early. Produces a high yield of good sized tubers with white flesh of firm waxy texture, shallow eyes and good cooking qualities. Has a very fine skin finish, making Pentland Lustre a nice show variety. Susceptible to gangrene and growth cracks with some resistance to blight, drought, common scab and eelworm. Foliage is of medium height with upright growth.

Picasso (1994)

A beautiful round, oval, part-coloured variety, maturing as an early maincrop. Produces a very high yield of nicely shaped uniform tubers with shallow eyes, cream flesh of firm texture and exceptional cooking qualities, especially for baking, boiling and roasting. Has good all round resistance to most potato diseases with a high resistance to common scab, and is eelworm resistant. Makes a top show variety.

Pink Fir Apple (1880)

A very old variety maturing as a late maincrop. Very popular because of its superb new potato flavour which lasts well into the new year. It produces long thin tubers with pink skin which can be eaten or removed after boiling. Flesh is cream with firm waxy texture. To obtain large tubers remove surplus sprouts prior to planting. Susceptible to leafroll and blight. An excellent salad potato.

Premiere (1987)

A round oval white variety maturing as a first early. Tubers are shallow-eyed. Flesh is cream and of floury/waxy texture with excellent flavour. Cooking qualities are excellent. Has good resistance to leafroll, virus X and virus Y. Resistant to potato cyst nematode (R.O. pathotype). Non-immune to wart disease. Foliage is of medium height.

Provost (1981)

A round oval white variety maturing as a first early. Eyes are shallow. Flesh is white and of firm semi-floury texture. Produces a good yield of nicely shaped tubers of reasonable cooking quality with some all round resistance to most diseases found in the garden. Foliage is of medium height.

Ratte (1872)

This old variety matures as a second early. Flesh is yellow with firm waxy texture and good flavour. Produces many long tubers of regular shape. An excellent salad or boiled potato. To obtain large tubers remove surplus sprouts prior to planting. Susceptible to leafroll, blight and drought.

Record (1944)

An oval russet-skinned variety maturing as an early maincrop. This well known variety has good cooking qualities. Flesh is yellow and floury, eyes are medium. Widely used for chipping and jacket potatoes. Stores well over winter. Has good resistance to blight, spraing and common scab. Susceptible to internal bruising, blackleg and drought. Resistant to gangrene.

Red Cara (1976)

A round oval red variety maturing as a late maincrop. Produces a huge crop of nicely shaped tubers of semi-floury/waxy texture with cream flesh and shallow eyes. Has good cooking qualities and is a first class baking potato. Has good resistance to after cooking discolouration. High resistance to foliage and tuber blight, common scab and bruising. Susceptible to powdery scab and slug damage. Eelworm resistant variety. Foliage is tall.

Red Craig's Royal (1957)

An oval red variety maturing as a second early. Tubers are nicely shaped with shallow eyes, white flesh of floury texture with good cooking qualities. Excellent for potato salads, remaining firm when boiled. Has real potato flavour and keeps well in storage. Resistant to powdery scab, drought and spaing. Susceptible to external damage and hair cracking.

Red Duke of York (1942)

Oval red variety maturing as a first early. Tubers are shallow-eyed. Flesh is cream and of floury texture with good cooking qualities. An excellent early baking potato, has nice flavour. Susceptible to leafroll, tuber blight and virus Y. Non-immune to wart disease. Foliage is of medium height. Also known as Rode Eersteling.

Red King Edward (1916)

A long oval red variety maturing as an early maincrop. Produces a moderate crop of good sized tubers with shallow to medium eyes. Flesh is of cream floury texture. Has good all-round cooking qualities. Differs only in colour from the original King Edward. Resistant to common scab, susceptible to wart disease, blight, virus Y and drought.

Red Pontiac (1954)

A round red variety maturing as an early maincrop. Produces a huge crop of large tubers of waxy texture with cream flesh and medium eyes. A top class baking potato. Has good resistance to gangrene and blight. Seed of this variety could be difficult to find in the U.K. Performs well from small seed. (An American variety).

Redskin (1934)

A round, red variety maturing as an early maincrop. Eyes are medium to deep, flesh is cream with a floury texture. Flavour is excellent, good for boiling and chipping. A similar variety to Kerr's Pink but tubers are larger. Growth is vigorous and of medium height to tall. Keeps well in over-winter storage, crops well on heavy soil.

Robinia (1983)

A long red variety maturing as a first early. Tubers are shallow-eyed with light yellow flesh and of waxy texture. Produces a high yield of even sized tubers. With good cooking qualities, with some resistance to tuber blight, susceptible to external damage and virus Y.

Rocket (1989)

A round white variety maturing as a true first early. Produces a good yield of medium sized tubers. Flesh is pure white and of firm waxy texture with good flavour and all round cooking qualities. No after-cooking discolouration. Eyes are of medium depth. Performs well under polythene, glass or container grown crops. Prone to growth cracks. Foliage is of medium height. Has good resistance to common scab, drought, blackleg and is eelworm resistant.

Revelino (1979)

A round, oval, white variety maturing as a first early. Produces a high yield of medium sized tubers with shallow to medium eyes. Flesh is light yellow and of semi-waxy texture. Cooking qualities are good with high resistance to after-cooking discolouration. Has good resistance to common scab and drought with average resistance to most other potato diseases. Resistance to R.O.I. cyst nematode.

Romano (1978) *below*

A beautiful round, oval red variety maturing as an early maincrop. Tubers are shallow-eyed, flesh is cream and of firm waxy texture. A good cooker staying very firm on boiling, with good resistance to skin spot, tuber and foliage blight, dry rot and bruising. Resistant to virus Y. Susceptible to leafroll virus and drought. A good variety for exhibition.

Roseval (1950)

A long oval red variety maturing as an early maincrop. Produces a good yield of medium sized tubers with shallow to medium eyes. Flesh is a dark yellow and of waxy texture. As this variety is not grown in the U.K. little is known about its qualities. Mostly grown in France for salad use. French grown ware does appear in U.K. stores at times.

Royal Kidney (1889)

A long oval white variety maturing as a second early. Tubers are of semi-waxy texture with cream flesh and shallow eyes. Has a real potato taste. Introduced over 100 years ago and still in cultivation. Has some resistance to most potato diseases.

Rubinia (1983)

A long oval pink variety maturing as a first early. Eyes are of medium depth. Flesh is light yellow and of firm waxy texture. Has fairly good cooking qualities with good resistance to most potato diseases. Foliage is of medium height and spreading.

Russet Burbank (1880)

A long russet-skinned variety maturing as a late maincrop. Produces a good yield of good sized tubers of semi-floury texture with medium eyes and cream flesh. An excellent variety for French fries. Susceptible to blight, spaing, drought and virus X. Mostly grown for processing. Seed may be difficult to find. (An American variety).

Samba (1989)

A long oval white variety maturing as an early maincrop. Produces a moderate yield of medium sized tubers. Eyes are of medium depth, flesh is yellow and of waxy texture with reasonable cooking qualities. Mostly used as a salad potato. This variety is not widely grown in the U.K.

Sangre (1991)

A beautiful round, bright red variety maturing as an early maincrop. Produces a good yield of nicely shaped tubers with white flesh of semi-waxy texture. Eyes are of medium depth all round. Cooking qualities are good. Has good resistance to most potato diseases. Keeps well in over-winter storage. Has scored some awards on the show bench since its introduction.

Sante (1985) *below*

A round oval white variety maturing as an early maincrop. Produces a good yield of uniform shaped tubers with shallow eyes and cream flesh of firm semi-floury/waxy texture. Cooking qualities are good and reasonably free from after-cooking blackening. Has good resistance to foliage and tuber blight, common scab, dry rot, bruising and powdery scab. Foliage is of medium height. Sante is eelworm resistant.

Saturna (1964) *above*

A short oval, white variety maturing as an early maincrop. Eye depth is shallow to medium, flesh is yellow and of floury texture, free from after-cooking discolouration. An excellent baking potato. Foliage is of medium height, has good resistance to gangrene, tuber blight and common scab.

Saxon (1992)

A long oval white variety maturing as a second early. Produces a good yield of even sized tubers of pale yellow flesh with shallow eyes and of semi-floury texture. Excellent for baking and chipping. Has good resistance to gangrene, drought, blackleg and after cooking discolouration.

Sharpes Express (1901)

A long white variety maturing as a first early. Eyes are shallow with raised eyebrows, flesh is yellow and of floury texture, very popular as a jacket potato and as an early scraper. Has excellent flavour, well worth growing. Foliage is of medium height. Susceptible to tuber blight and wart disease.

Shepody (1988)

A long white variety maturing as an early maincrop. Eyes are of medium depth, flesh is white and of dry texture. Has good resistance to gangrene, dry rot, drought, blackleg, powdery and common scab, with good resistance to after-cooking discolouration. Grown mostly for processing rather than garden use.

Shula (1986)

A long oval pink-eyed variety maturing as an early maincrop. Produces a good yield of nicely shaped tubers with cream flesh of excellent flavour and texture. A first class baking and boiling potato. Has shallow eyes and a nice skin finish making Shula a top flight exhibition variety. Suscep-tible to skin spot and virus Y. Intermediate reaction to common scab and tuber blight. Has high resistance to drought, blackleg and after cooking discolouration.

Sierra (1991)

A round, white variety maturing as an early maincrop. Produces a high yield of good sized tubers with shallow eyes. Cream flesh of dry texture has good fry colour and absorbs less oil in cooking. Has good resistance to after-cooking discolouration, dry rot, drought, blackleg and bruising.

Skirza (1986)

A long, oval, pink variety maturing as a second early. Flesh is pale yellow, produces a good yield of good sized tubers. Excellent as a boiled potato. Resistant to virus Y and golden eelworm and has good resistance to tuber blight. Foliage is medium height to tall.

Spunta (1976)

A long, oval, white variety maturing as a second early. Produces a moderate to high yield of good sized tubers of floury texture, shallow eyes and yellow flesh. Cooking qualities are good, with high resistance to blight. Susceptible to common scab and external damage.

Stemster (1986)

A long, oval, pink variety maturing as an early maincrop. Produces a very high yield of large tubers. Has good all round cooking qualities. Tubers are shallow-eyed with yellow flesh of firm waxy texture. With a mild flavour and no after cooking discolouration. Has good resistance to slug damage, gangrene, drought, blackleg and powdery scab and is eelworm resistant.

Stroma (1988)

A long oval red variety maturing as a second early. Produces a high yield of good sized tubers of firm waxy texture. Flesh is light yellow with a mild flavour and no appreciable after-cooking discolouration. Good all round cooking qualities with good resistance to blight, skin spot, common scab, drought, blackleg, bruising, powdery scab and slug damage. Foliage is of medium height.

Swift (1993)

A round to oval white variety maturing as a first early. Produces a high yield of nicely shaped smooth skinned tubers with shallow eyes. Flesh is creamy-white and of firm waxy texture with excellent all round cooking qualities. Has good resistance to most potato diseases and is eelworm resistant. A lovely potato. Foliage is low to medium height (recommended for exhibition).

Symphonia (1994)

An oval, red variety maturing as an early maincrop. Produces a good yield of uniform shaped tubers with superior skin finish with shallow eyes and light yellow flesh of waxy texture, making Symphonia an excellent pre-pack variety, with good all round cooking qualities. Has good resistance to most potato diseases with resistance to potato cyst nematode (R.O. pathotype).

Teena (1986)

A round white variety maturing as a first early. Produces a moderate yield of good sized tubers with shallow eyes. Floury texture and yellow flesh. Has a tendency to discolour after cooking with reasonable all-round cooking qualities. Has good resistance to most potato diseases.

Torridon (1988)

A long oval white variety maturing as an early maincrop. Eyes are of medium depth. Flesh is light yellow and of semi-floury/waxy texture. Has good resistance to foliage and tuber blight with some resistance to common scab and leafroll. Susceptible to wart disease. Foliage is of medium height. (Cooking qualities are reasonably good).

Tristar (1993)

A long oval red variety maturing as an early maincrop. Produces a good yield of large tubers, with shallow eyes and cream flesh of waxy texture. Has excellent cooking qualities and good resistance to gangrene, skin spot, foliage and tuber blight with high resistance to common scab. Foliage is of medium height (Eelworm Resistant).

Ulster Chieftain (1938)

An oval white variety maturing as a first early. An excellent variety for wind swept sites as the haulms are short. Ulster Chieftain is a fast grower and bulks early. Eyes are shallow to medium, flesh is white of waxy texture. An excellent early roaster and scraper. Susceptible to common scab, blight and late frost damage.

Ulster Prince (1947)

A long white variety maturing as a first early. Produces good sized tubers with white flesh of firm waxy texture and shallow eyes. Forces well under glass or polythene. True long whites are very few in the show world. Ulster Prince is a good long white for exhibition when well grown. Has good resistance to drought. Susceptible to tuber blight and spraing. Has poor frost recovery.

Ulster Sceptre (1964)

A long oval white variety maturing as a first early. Produces a high yield of bold tubers. Flesh is cream and of waxy texture with good cooking qualities. At its best early in the season, does not keep well in storage.

Sprouts rapidly in spring, eyes are of medium depth. Has good resistance to drought. Susceptible to mechanical damage, gangrene and spraing with some resistance to after cooking discolouration.

Up-To-Date (1894)

An oval white variety maturing as a late maincrop. Has good cooking qualities. Tubers are shallow-eyed with white flesh and of firm waxy texture. This lovely potato was introduced over 100 years ago and is still with us. Drought resistant, susceptible to blight, common scab and wart disease.

Valor (1994)

A lovely round, oval, white variety maturing as an early maincrop. Produces a good yield of nicely shaped tubers with shallow eyes and white flesh of firm texture. The cooking quality is excellent, recommended for boiling, baking and chipping. Valor has scored some success on the show bench but tubers can be somewhat flat. Has good resistance to blight. Susceptible to gangrene. Resistant to potato cyst nematode (R.O. pathotype).

Vanessa (1968)

A long pink variety maturing as a first early with cream flesh, shallow eyes, and a waxy texture. Stays firm on cooking, has good resistance to slug damage. Susceptible to blight and spraing. Good for exhibition.

Windsor (1995)

A round oval white variety, maturing as a second early. Flesh is pale yellow and of semi-floury texture. Eyes are of medium depth. An excellent variety for all round table use. Has good resistance to bruising, drought, blackleg and after-cooking discolouration.

Winston (1992)

A beautiful round, oval, white variety maturing as a first early. Produces a good yield of nicely shaped large tubers with shallow eyes and cream flesh of firm waxy texture with good all round cooking qualities and a very fine skin finish, making Winston a top flight exhibition variety. Has scored high marks on the show bench since its introduction. Has good resistance to most potato diseases and is eelworm resistant.

Wilja (1972) *below*

A long oval white variety maturing as a second early. A high yielding variety. Produces numerous tubers of uniform shape and size, of good table quality with shallow eyes. Flesh is pale yellow and of firm waxy texture. Wilja is at its best before Christmas. Has moderate resistance to foliage and tuber blight. With good resistance to after-cooking discolouration, and some resistance to blackleg, common scab and drought. Susceptible to virus Y.

Yukon Gold (1980)

A round part-coloured variety maturing as a second early. With shallow eyes, yellow flesh and of moderately dry texture suitable for early season baking and French fries. Has good resistance to cooking discolouration with some resistance to blight, drought, common scab, skin spot and blackleg.

Chapter IX

Potato Varieties of Yesterday

Aberdonian (1907)
An oval white, maturing as an early main-crop. Eyes are deep with raised eyebrows. Flesh is yellow, sprouts are pink. Foliage is of medium height, spreading and bushy. Stems are numerous, branching freely.

Adirondack (1881)
A round red, maturing as a second early. Eyes are shallow. Flesh is white. Foliage is of medium height, upright and open.

Ally (1915)
A round to oval yellow, maturing as an early maincrop. Eyes are shallow saucer shaped, few and close together on the shoulder. Flesh is a soft white. Foliage is of medium height.

America (1876)
This variety is identical with the old American variety Irish Cobbler. A round white maturing as a first early. Tubers are dented at the stem end. Eyes are deep. Flesh is white.

Ardneal Rose (1916)
An oval pink, maturing as an early main-crop. Eyes are of medium depth, eyebrows are long. Flesh is white and of semi-waxy texture. Foliage is of medium height and spreading.

Arran Chief (1911)
A round white (somewhat flat), maturing as an early maincrop. Usually has a purple spot at the heel during the growing season. Eyes are medium. Flesh is white and floury.

Arran Comrade (1918)
A round white (somewhat flat), maturing as a second early. Eyes are shallow and on the shoulder. Flesh is white and of semi-waxy texture.

Arran Rose (1919)
An oval rose coloured, maturing as a first early. Eyes are shallow. Flesh is white. Foliage is medium to tall and upright.

Balcarres (1910)
A round flat white, slightly dented at heel, maturing as a second early. Medium eyes and ridged eyebrows. Foliage is of medium height and upright.

Balvaird (1920)
An oval white, maturing as a second early. Eyes are medium to shallow. Flesh is white. Foliage is of medium height and spreading. Stems are numerous and tinged red-purple, especially at the base.

Barley Bounty (1905)
A long oval white, maturing as an early maincrop. Eyes are shallow and on point. Flesh is white. Foliage is of medium height and spreading. Stems numerous, tinged red-purple, especially at the base.

Beauty of Bute (1890)
A round white with pink markings, dented at heel, maturing as an early maincrop. Eyes are large and rounded, medium to deep often with raised eyebrows. Flesh is white, sprouts pink. Foliage is tall, open and upright, spreading later. Stem wings are broad.

Benalt (1900)

A round, flat, dented at heel, maturing as an early maincrop. Eyes are medium ridged with traces of pink. Flesh is pale yellow. Foliage is of medium height to tall, upright and spreading stems are thin.

Ben Cruachan (1904)

An oval white, maturing as a late maincrop. Eyes are shallow to medium. Flesh is a soft white. Foliage is tall and upright, stems branching very freely.

Ben Lomond (1923)

An oval white maturing as a second early. Eyes are shallow. Flesh is white. Foliage is of medium height and compact.

Bishop (1912)

A long white, maturing as a late maincrop. Eyes are small and shallow. Flesh is yellow and of semi-waxy texture. Foliage is strong, upright and open.

Blue Catriona (1979)

A long oval blue, maturing as a second early. Eyes are shallow. Flesh is soft white with a tinge of lemon and of floury texture.

Blue Gloss (1924)

A round white, dented at heel, maturing as an early maincrop. Eyes are deep recessed, numerous and with raised eyebrows. Flesh is yellow, sprouts are blue. The tubers are numerous and small. Foliage is of medium height to tall, upright, spreading later. Stems are mottled blue-purple. Leaf close and short.

Blue Grey (1924)

A round white, maturing as a late maincrop. Eyes are small and shallow to medium, saucer shaped. Flesh is white. Tubers are small with tendency to second growth. The scale leaves are blue. Foliage is of medium height to tall, upright and spreading later in the season. Stems numerous and slender.

Blue President (1901)

A round white, sometimes blotched purple round the eyes and heel. Eyes are medium to deep and recessed. Flesh is pale yellow, sometimes streaked blue. Foliage is tall and upright. Stems mottled dark purple. Strong branching leaves, open and rigid midribs slightly coloured in younger leaves.

Bobbie Burns (1915)

A round white, maturing as an early maincrop. Eyes are shallow and saucer shaped. Flesh is white. Foliage is of medium height to tall, upright, spreading later, opening out from centre stems, branching wings, broad leaf, open leaflets dull medium green narrow pointed.

Bravo (1886)

A round white (somewhat flat), maturing as an early maincrop. Eyes are medium and ridged. Flesh is pale yellow, sprouts blue-purple. Foliage is of medium height and spreading. Stems are mottled purple at base, numerous and thin.

Buchan Beauty (1922)

A round, dented at heel, yellow with blue-purple markings. Maturing as a late maincrop. Eyes are deep. Flesh is yellow. Foliage is tall and upright. Stems are mottled blue-purple especially at base.

Burnhead (1918)

A round white (somewhat flat), maturing as an early maincrop. Eyes are medium to deep with raised eyebrows. Flesh is white with a tinge of cream, sprouts are blue. Runners are numerous, foliage is medium to tall, spreading and compact, stems branching freely. Leaves are open and rigid.

Cardinal (1916)

A red kidney, maturing as an early maincrop. Flesh is red, colour is mostly lost on boiling and texture becomes soft and watery. This variety has not been widely grown due to its flesh colour. Foliage is low to medium height, grown mostly as a novelty. A very interesting variety.

Celt (1920)

An oval to round white, maturing as a late maincrop. Eyes are on point and are medium to deep with raised eyebrows. Flesh is white. Foliage is of medium height to tall, vigorous and compact and branching excessively.

Celurca (1896)

An oval white, maturing as a late maincrop. Eyes are shallow to medium. Flesh is a soft white. Foliage is of medium height and upright with stems branching very freely.

Champion (1876)

A round white, distinctly dented at heel, often has a blue-purple splash at the heel in the growing season. Eyes are very deep. Flesh is yellow and of floury texture. Matures as a late maincrop.

Claymore (1927)

A round white, maturing as a late maincrop. Eyes are shallow and close together. Flesh is white. Foliage is tall, upright, dense and vigorous.

Colourless (1891)

A round white, dented at heel, maturing as an early maincrop. Eyes are medium. Flesh is white, sprouts pink, runners numerous. Foliage is tall and upright, stems are numerous, branching freely, leaf open very rigid and short.

Congo (1900)

A long black maturing as a late maincrop. Flesh is purple and of sludgy texture, tubers are of small to medium size and knobbly. Growth is vigorous and upright, this variety is grown more for a novelty rather than a table potato, a very interesting variety.

Conquest (1912)

A round white, maturing as a second early. Eyes are shallow and ridged on the point. Flesh is white. Scale leaves are light blue (sprouts blue). Foliage is low to medium height and spreading. Leaflets are light to medium green, glossy, arched and drooping, generally with a purple mark.

Corona (1912)

A round white, maturing as a late maincrop. Eyes are shallow and rounded. Flesh is a soft white. Foliage is tall, upright and spreading, stems are mottled purple, especially near the base.

Coronation (1958)

A round white, maturing as a first early. Eyes are shallow and saucer shaped and on point of tuber. Flesh is white towards maturity, there is often a pink spot on the stem end of the tuber. Foliage is low to medium height.

Crimson Beauty (1909)

An oval deep pink, maturing as a first early. Eyes are very shallow. Flesh is white, tinged pink. Foliage is low to medium height. Stems are slightly mottled red-purple.

Croft (1975)

A round oval white variety, maturing as an early maincrop. Eyes are shallow. Flesh is cream and of waxy texture. Foliage is of medium height and upright.

Crusader (1918)

A long kidney white, maturing as a second early. Eyes are shallow and saucer shaped, usually on the shoulder, those on the sides with slightly raised eyebrows. Flesh is white. Foliage is of medium height to tall and upright.

Dargal Early (1917)

A long to oval yellow, maturing as a second early. Eyes are shallow, those on the side having raised eyebrows. Flesh is yellow. Foliage is of medium height and spreading.

Dean (1922)

An oval white with traces of blue-purple colour about the eyes at harvesting time, turning light purple on exposure. Eyes are medium to shallow saucer shaped. Flesh is white.

Dominion (1916)

An oval white, maturing as a late maincrop. Eyes are shallow to medium. Flesh is white. Foliage is tall and upright. Stems are blue-purple branching.

Dr McIntosh (1944)

A long oval white, maturing as an early maincrop. Eyes are shallow, flesh is white and waxy. Foliage is of medium height.

Duke of Perth (1929)

An oval white, maturing as a late maincrop. Eyes are shallow with long eyebrows. Flesh is white. Foliage is tall, upright, dense and vigorous. Stems are strong, branching freely.

Dumfries Favourite (1910)

A round white maturing as a late maincrop. Eyes are shallow and ridged. Flesh is a soft white. Foliage is of medium height to tall and spreading.

Dunaverney (1898)

An oval white, maturing as a late maincrop. Eyes are shallow to medium. Flesh is a soft white. Foliage is tall and upright. Stems slightly mottled purple branching freely.

Dundarave (1906)

A long oval white, maturing as an early maincrop. Eyes are shallow to medium. Ridged on the point. Flesh is pale yellow. Foliage is of medium height to tall. Upright open stems branching freely.

Dunnottar Castle (1915)

An oval white, maturing as a first early. Eyes are shallow. Flesh is white. Foliage is low to medium height.

Dunvegan Castle (1922)

A round white maturing as a first early. Eyes are shallow and saucer shaped. Flesh is pale yellow. Foliage is low to medium height. Stems are upright and are slightly mottled purple. Leaves are open and rigid.

Early Pink Champion (1919)

A round pink, dented at heel, maturing as a first early. Eyes are medium and on point of tuber. Eyebrows are long and ridged. Flesh is white. Foliage is low to medium height, upright and spreading. Stem branching tinged pink.

Early Rose (1861)

An oval pointed pale pink, maturing as a first early. Eyes are shallow and numerous. Flesh is white streaked red. Foliage is low to medium height, upright and spreading.

Eclipse (1900)

An oval white, maturing as a first early. Eyes are shallow and almost on the point of tuber. Flesh is white. Texture is semi-waxy. Foliage is of medium height.

Edgecote Purple (1900)

A long oval purple, maturing as an early maincrop. Flesh is light yellow and of firm waxy texture. Eyes are shallow to medium with raised eyebrows. Cooking qualities are excellent. Foliage is medium to tall. This variety was never grown in large quantities.

Edinchip (1908)

A long oval white, maturing as an early maincrop. Eyes are small and shallow. Flesh is a soft white. Foliage is of medium height and spreading. Stems are slightly tinged pink.

Eightyfold (1894).

A round pale purple, maturing as a first early. Eyes are shallow. Flesh is white. Foliage is of medium height and upright spreading later. Stems are dark blue-purple with purple midrib. Leaflets light to medium green, large bright and drooping, secondary leaflets numerous.

Evergood (1899)

An oval white, maturing as an early maincrop. Eyes are shallow and on the point of the tuber. Flesh is a soft white. Foliage erect with drooping tops.

Field Marshall (1924)

An oval white, maturing as a late maincrop. Eyes are shallow and on the point of the tuber. Flesh is white. Foliage is of medium height to tall and spreading.

Fiftyfold (1882)

An oval white, maturing as a second early. Eyes are shallow. Flesh is white. Foliage is of medium height.

Flourball (1895)

A round pink (somewhat flat), dented at heel, maturing as an early maincrop. Flesh is white and of floury texture. Foliage is of medium height and spreading. Stems are slightly tinged pink.

Footprint (1916)

A round flat white, slightly dented at the heel, maturing as a late maincrop. Eyes are shallow to medium with raised eyebrows. Flesh is white. Foliage is tall, upright and dense. Stems are slightly mottled purple.

Fortyfold (1836)

A round, dented at heel, yellow splashed with purple, maturing as an early maincrop. Eyes are shallow to deep. Flesh is white. Foliage is of medium height, upright but becomes straggling.

Gigantic (1924)

A long oval white, maturing as an early maincrop. Eyes are shallow. Flesh is a soft white. Foliage is of medium height, branches are spindly. Leaf open rigid, midrib faintly coloured at base of stalks.

Glasgow Favourite (1921)

A round oval white, maturing as a late maincrop. Eyes are shallow and rounded. Flesh is white. Foliage is of medium height and upright. Leaf rigid, leaflets are medium green.

Gladstone (1932)

A round white with red markings, maturing as an early maincrop. Eyes are of medium depth. Flesh is white and of semi waxy texture.

Granispud (1915)

An oval-kidney white, maturing as an early maincrop. Eyes are shallow to medium. Flesh is white. Foliage is of medium height and upright, sprawling later. Leaf rigid and very open.

Glen Almond (1925)

A round flat white, maturing as a late maincrop. Eyes are shallow. Flesh is pale yellow. Sprouts are blue. Foliage is of medium height to tall with an open appearance. Stem branching mottled purple.

Golden Lass (1912)

An oval yellow, maturing as a late maincrop. Eyes are shallow and saucer shaped. Flesh is yellow. Foliage is vigorous and spreading and of medium height to tall.

Golden Marvel (1901)

An oval white, slightly dented at heel, maturing as a late maincrop. Eyes are medium with raised eyebrows. Flesh is pale yellow. Foliage is tall and upright. Stems are slightly mottled purple and branching freely.

Great Scot (1909)

A round yellow (somewhat flat), heel generally dented during the growing season. Eyes can have a touch of white and are shallow to medium (saucer shaped). Flesh is white and of floury texture. A tall upright grower.

Gregor Cups (1903)

A round, dented at heel pink, maturing as a late maincrop. Eyes are deep. Flesh is white, sprouts pink. Foliage is tall, coarse and open. Stems are strong and branching freely, mottled red-purple, wings are marked and crinkled. Leaf rigid and short.

Harbinger (1894)

A round (flat), dented at heel, white, maturing as a first early. Eyes are medium to deep and saucer shaped, generally on point of tuber. Flesh is white. Foliage is low and spreading.

Herd Laddie (1908)

A round blue-purple maturing as a second early. Eyes are shallow. Flesh is white with a ring of blue. Foliage is of medium height and upright, sprawling later.

Imune Ashleaf (1891)

A long oval white, maturing as a first early. Eyes are shallow and on the point of the tuber often with raised eyebrows. Flesh is yellow. Foliage is of medium height and spreading.

Incomer (1923)

An oval (oblong) white, maturing as a late maincrop. Eyes are shallow and saucer shaped. Flesh is white. Foliage is tall, upright and dense. Stems are strong, branching freely.

International Kidney (1879)

A long oval yellow, maturing as an early maincrop. Eyes are shallow ridged. Flesh is yellow. Foliage is of medium height to tall. Upright stems are blue-purple (Also known as Jersey Royal).

Irish Chieftain (1916)

An oval white, dented at heel, maturing as a late maincrop (very late). Eyes are medium and mostly on the point of tuber. Flesh is white, sprouts are blue. Foliage is of medium height to tall, strong and branching stems are mottled purple.

Irish Queen (1910)

A round yellow splashed pink (sometimes whole pink), maturing as a late maincrop. Eyes are deep. Flesh is white and floury with excellent taste.

John Bull (1913)

A round white with pink markings, dented at heel, maturing as an early maincrop. Eyes are shallow, open and large, eyebrows are long and slightly raised. Flesh is white. Sprouts are medium pink. Foliage is tall and upright. Stems are branching, wings inconspicuous, leaves close, ridged and point upwards.

Katie Grover (1921)

An oval yellow with red eyes, maturing as a second early. Eyes are shallow but deep in large tubers, eyebrows are distinct. Flesh is white. Foliage is low to medium height.

Keay's Champion (1903)

An oval white, tinged pale pink at stem end, maturing as an early maincrop. Eyes are shallow and saucer shaped. Flesh is white, and sprouts are pink. Foliage is tall and upright. Stems are slightly mottled purple.

Kenzy (1987)

A round oval pink maturing as a late maincrop. Eyes are shallow. Flesh is light yellow and of waxy texture. Foliage is of medium height and upright.

Kepplestone Kidney (1919)

A long oval blue purple, maturing as an early maincrop. Eyes are shallow often with raised eyebrows. Flesh is yellow and of floury texture. Foliage is of medium height to tall.

King George (1911)

An oval white, occasionally with a touch of pink at the heel and the rose end, matures as a second early. Eyes are medium and on point of tuber. Those on the side of the tuber with raised eyebrows. Flesh is white and of waxy texture.

Langworthy (1876)

An oval white, maturing as a late maincrop. Eyes are shallow and saucer shaped with raised eyebrows. Flesh is white to lemon colour. Foliage is tall, upright and vigorous.

Lochar (1915)

A round white, very delicately pink when immature, with pink in the eyes and heel, matures as a late maincrop. Eyes are medium to deep and saucer shaped. Foliage is medium height to tall and compact.

Lord Rosebery (1920)

A round deep pink, maturing as a second early. Eyes are shallow to medium. Flesh is white. Foliage is of medium height spreading with flat tops.

Lord Scone (1925)

A long oval white, maturing as a second early. Eyes are shallow to medium. Flesh is white. Foliage is of medium height and spreading. Stem branching freely. Leaf very open, leaflet medium to dark green.

Lumpers (1806)

Round oval white, maturing as an early maincrop. Eyes are deep. Flesh is white and waxy, yields are excellent. Taste is poor, culinary use is limited. Now grown as a novelty only. One of the oldest varieties in cultivation (tubers are knobbly). A very interesting variety.

Lymm Gray (1903)

A round white (somewhat flat), heel is pink when immature, maturing as a second early. Eyes are small and deep. Flesh is white, sprouts pink. Foliage is of medium height to tall. Compact with slightly drooping tops. Stems are tinged red-purple, leaves are fairly open, wings broad with large waves.

Magnificent (1918)

An oval white, maturing as an early maincrop. Eyes are medium to deep. Flesh is white. Foliage is of medium height, vigorous and spreading, stem branching, leaf open with dark green leaflets, dull, large, rounded and slightly wrinkled.

Magnum Bonum (1876)

A long oval white, maturing as a late maincrop. Eyes are shallow and on the point. Flesh is white, sprouts faint pink. Foliage tall and upright, branching early. Wings of stem freely waved. Leaf open. Midribs with red marks at base.

Mains Surprise (1919)

An oval white, maturing as an early maincrop. Eyes are medium to deep and very small. Flesh is a soft white. Foliage is of medium height and spreading, stems mottled purple, branching fairly freely. Leaf rigid, long and fairly close, leaflets medium green and glossy.

Main's Triumph (1923)

An oval white maturing as a late maincrop. Eyes are medium recessed. Flesh is white. Foliage is tall, upright and vigorous. Stem branching mottled dark purple, wings slightly waved and broad. Leaf rigid, midrib tinged red-purple.

Marquis of Bute (1915).

A round white pink-eyed, maturing as a second early. Eyes are shallow to medium. Flesh is white. Foliage is of medium height to tall.

Maud Meg (1921)

A long to oval dark red, maturing as a late maincrop. Eyes are shallow to medium and on point of tuber. Eyebrows are long and raised. Flesh is yellow. Foliage is of medium height to tall.

Mauve Queen (1915)

A round blue-purple, maturing as an early maincrop. Eyes are shallow to medium, eyebrows long. Flesh is white, sprouts blue. Foliage is of medium height and spreading, stems are strong.

Maybole (1906)

An oval white, maturing as a first early. Eyes are deep. Flesh is white, sprouts are pink. Foliage is low and spreading. Leaf long, leaflets markedly large and light to medium green, cupped and thin with slightly waved margins.

May Queen (1900)

A long oval white maturing as a first early. Eyes are shallow. Flesh is a soft white and of floury/waxy texture. Foliage is of medium height.

Meins (Early Round) (1916)

A round part-coloured, maturing as a second early. Eyes are of medium depth. Flesh is white. This variety was mostly grown by gardeners and was a useful show potato until more modern shallow eyed varieties came on the market.

Millars Beauty (1902)

An oval white, maturing as a second early. Eyes are very shallow. Flesh is white. Foliage is low to medium height and spreading. Stem branching, tinged red-purple at base and bases of leaflet stalks.

Myatt's Ashleaf (1847)

An oval white, maturing as a second early. Eyes are shallow to medium. Those on sides of tuber with raised eyebrows. Flesh is yellow. Sprouts blue scale leaves, sometimes tinged light blue. Foliage is of medium height.

Ninetyfold (1897)

An oval white, maturing as a first early. Eyes are shallow on point, often with raised eyebrows on side. Flesh is a soft white and of waxy texture. Foliage is of medium height.

Nithsdale (1916)

An oval white, maturing as a second early. Eyes are shallow to medium. Flesh is white. Foliage is of medium height to tall, growth is upright and strong.

Norna (1909)

A long oval white, maturing as a second early. Eyes are very shallow on point. Flesh is white. Sprouts are faint pink. Foliage is of medium height to tall, upright, spreading later. Stems branched, leaves drooping and open. Midribs pink tinged, especially at the bases of leaflet stalks.

Nonesuch (1918)

A round flat white, dented at heel, maturing as a first early. Tubers are shallow eyed. Flesh is white, sprouts are pink. Foliage upright and of medium height, sprawling later. Stems are tinged red-purple. Marked angular leaf, close and short.

Northern Star (1900)

A round white, maturing as a late maincrop, has a small spot of pink in the eyes and the heel, especially during the growing season. Eyes are medium. Flesh is white. Foliage is tall, upright and compact.

Oran Beauty (1910)

An oval white, maturing as a second early. Eyes are shallow and ridged. Flesh is white. Foliage is low to medium height and spreading. Stems are green becoming tinged pink. Wings are slightly waved.

Peach Bloom (1923)
A round, dented at heel, white splashed deep pink, maturing as a late maincrop. Eyes are medium to deep. Flesh is white. Foliage is tall and upright, stems are tinged red-purple with numerous thin branches.

Peerless (1918)
A round (flat) blue-purple, maturing as a late maincrop. Eyes are shallow and open with long eyebrows. Flesh is a soft white. Foliage is of medium height to tall and spreading. Stems are mottled dark blue-purple.

Perth Favourite (1925)
A round (somewhat flat), white maturing as a late maincrop. Eyes are small, shallow and close together on shoulder. Flesh is white. Foliage is tall and upright, stems are slightly mottled purple (branching).

Pink Pearl (1921)
An oval-kidney dark pink, maturing as an early maincrop. Eyes are shallow to medium. Flesh deep yellow, sprouts are pink. Foliage is tall and upright. Stem branching mottled red-purple. Branches spindly, wings waved.

President (1901)
A round white (somewhat flat). Eyes are medium and saucer shaped. Flesh is white and of firm texture, haulms are tall, upright and compact.

Pride of Bute (1918)
A kidney (pear-shaped) blue-purple, maturing as an early maincrop. Eyes are shallow. Flesh is white, sprouts are blue. Foliage is tall, stems mottled purple, darker at base, wings are slightly waved. Leaf open, midrib purple.

Puritan (1895)
An oval white, maturing as a first early. Eyes are medium, eyebrows are long and raised. Flesh is snow-white and soft. Foliage is of medium height. Stems are tinged pink towards maturity.

Raeburn's Gregor Cups (1924)
A round pink, maturing as an early maincrop. Eyes are medium. Flesh is white, sprouts pink. Foliage is of medium height to tall and upright. Stems mottled dark red-purple, branching fairly freely, wings of main stem fairly waved. Leaf open and rigid.

Ranfurly Red (1920)
A round pink, maturing as an early maincrop. Eyes are medium to deep. Flesh is white. Foliage is of medium height to tall and upright, stems are mottled pink. Leaf open and drooping, midrib tinged pink.

Reading Russet (1882)
A round pink maturing as a second early. Eyes are shallow and close together. Flesh is white, sprouts are pink. Foliage is low to medium height and spreading, stems are mottled red-purple. Leaf open, slightly drooping.

Rector (1916)
A round medium pink with a deeper colour in the eyes, maturing as a late maincrop. Eyes are medium to deep. Flesh is white with a tint of pale yellow, sprouts are pink. Foliage is tall upright, vigorous and branching.

Red Salad (1958)

An oval red, maturing as an early maincrop. Flesh is pink and of waxy texture. This variety has never been grown commercially, but more as a novelty. Foliage is of medium height. A variety of great interest due to its pink flesh (found in collections only).

Response (1926)

An oval white, maturing as an early maincrop. Eyes are shallow to medium. Flesh is white. Foliage is tall and upright, stems branching and slightly tinged purple. Leaf open, leaflets large and medium to dark green.

Rhoderick Dhu (1919)

A round white (somewhat flat), dented at heel. Eyes are medium and close together on the shoulder. Flesh is white and semi-waxy. A tall, stout, upright grower.

Ringleader (1904)

A long oval white, maturing as a first early. Eyes are shallow to medium. Flesh is white, sprouts are pink. Foliage is low to medium height and spreading. Stems are tinged pink especially at the base. Leaves are open and drooping.

Rocks (1856)

A round white, deeply dented at heel, maturing as a late maincrop. Eyes are medium and deeply recessed on point. Flesh is a soft white, sprouts are pink. Foliage is of medium height to tall. Upright stems are mottled dark red-purple. Branching fairly freely, wings of main stems slightly waved. Leaf open and rigid.

Roseval (1950)

An oval red maturing as an early maincrop. Eyes are shallow. Flesh is yellow and of waxy texture. Excellent as a salad potato, produces a moderate yield of medium sized tubers. A French variety, seldom grown in the U.K.

Royal Stewart (1908)

A long oval white, maturing as a late maincrop. Eyes are shallow to medium. Flesh is a soft white, sprouts are blue. Foliage is tall and spreading. Stems are slightly mottled purple, branching freely. Branches are thick, wings of main stem slightly waved. Leaf rigid. Leaflets are medium green and rounded, slightly wrinkled (cupped).

Scottish Chief (1901)

A round (flat) white, maturing as an early maincrop. Eyes are shallow to medium and ridged, flesh is white, sprouts pink, second growth (cracking) frequent. Foliage is of medium height to tall and upright. Stem wings waved, leaf fairly open, exposing leaflet stalks which are medium to dark green.

Shamrock (1890)

A round pink (somewhat flat), dented at heel, maturing as a late maincrop. Eyes are shallow. Flesh is a soft white, sprouts pink. Foliage is of medium height and upright. Stems strong. Branching mottled red-purple. Leaf open, midrib dark red-purple.

Sharpe's Pink Seedling (1891)

A round pink maturing as an early maincrop. Eyes are shallow to medium. Flesh is white, sprouts are pink. Foliage is of medium height to tall. Stems are numerous, tinged red-purple, especially at the base. Leaf open and rigid, midrib dark red. Leaflets round and distinctly pointed, medium green and dull.

Sharpe's Victor (1891)

An oval white, maturing as an early maincrop. Eyes are shallow. Flesh is yellow, sprouts are blue. Foliage is low to medium height and spreading. Stems mottled blue-purple especially at base. Leaf rigid, leaflets broad, medium green, heart shaped at base, blunt.

Skerry Blue (1846)

A round, oval blue, maturing as a late maincrop. Eyes are deep. Flesh is cream. Foliage is of medium height.

Southesk (1925)

A round (somewhat flat) white, maturing as a late maincrop. Eyes are shallow and saucer shaped. Flesh is white. Foliage is tall and upright.

Spion Cop (1911)

Round white, maturing as an early maincrop. Eyes are shallow to medium and saucer shaped. Flesh is white, sprouts pink. Foliage is of medium height to tall, open and upright. Stems are mottled purple and branching, branches are spindly.

Stirling Castle (1914)

An oval white, maturing as an early maincrop. Eyes are shallow and open. Flesh is a soft white, sprouts are pink. Foliage is of medium height to tall spreading later with drooping tops. Stems are slightly tinged pink. Leaf drooping fairly close, leaflets are light to medium green and dull.

Stormont Enterprise (1969)

An oval white variety, maturing as an early maincrop. Eyes are of medium depth. Flesh is cream and of floury texture. Foliage is of medium height and close spreading.

Summit (1912)

A round white, maturing as a late maincrop. Eyes are shallow to medium. Flesh is white, sprouts pink. Foliage is tall, upright and vigorous. Stems are numerous, mottled red-purple, especially at base, wings are slightly waved. Leaf short, open and rigid.

Sutton's Abundance (1886)

An oval to round (flat) white, maturing as an early maincrop. Eyes are shallow and usually on the shoulder. Eyebrows are long and distinct. Flesh is white and of firm waxy texture.

Sutton's Early Regent (1882)

A round white (somewhat flat) maturing as a second early. Eyes are shallow and small. Flesh is a soft white, sprouts are pink. Foliage is low to medium height, vigorous and spreading. Stems are thin, mottled pink. Leaf fairly close. Leaflets light green and dull, secondary leaflets numerous, round.

Templar (1912)

An oval to round (flat) white, maturing as a late maincrop. Tubers are small to medium size. Eyes are very shallow. Flesh is white, runners profuse, long and blue tinted, sprouts are blue. Foliage is tall and upright with a very open appearance. Stems branching, mottled purple especially at base.

The Mac (1901)

An oval white, maturing as an early main-crop. Eyes are shallow to medium with raised eyebrows. Flesh is white. Foliage is tall and upright. Stems branching freely and of yellowish green. Leaf small and rigid, leaflet light to medium green (narrow).

The Massie (1906)

A round white, dented at heel, maturing as a second early. Eyes are medium rounded. Flesh is yellow, sprouts pink. Foliage is of medium height to tall and upright, spreading later. Stems are thin and numerous. Branching freely.

The Towse (1916)

A round deep pink with yellow blotches, maturing as a first early. Eyes are of medium depth. Flesh is yellow, sprouts pink. Foliage is of medium height and spreading. Stems are pink tinged and branching, leaf open, midribs pink.

Ulster Ensign (1946)

A long oval white, pink-eyed, maturing as second early. Eyes are shallow. Flesh is white and of waxy texture. Foliage is of medium height.

Ulster Premier (1944)

A long part-coloured variety, maturing as a first early. Eyes are shallow. Flesh is white and of waxy texture. Foliage is low and spreading.

Utility (1921)

A round (flat) pink, dented at heel, maturing as an early maincrop. Eyes are medium to deep. Flesh is white. Foliage is of medium height, spreading and vigorous.

Waverley (1920)

A long oval pink, maturing as an early main-crop. Eyes are of medium depth. Flesh is white and of semi-waxy texture. Cooking qualities are good. Foliage is of medium height and upright.

White City (1909)

A long oval yellow with a slight russet appearance, maturing as a late maincrop. Eyes are few and very shallow. Flesh is pale yellow, sprouts pink. Foliage is vigorous and spreading, tall and rigid.

Wild Rose (1901)

An oval white, maturing as a late maincrop. Eyes are shallow. Flesh is white, sprouts blue. Foliage is of medium height and spreading. Stems are slightly mottled purple. Leaf open, leaflets decidedly arched.

Windsor Castle (1900)

An oval white, maturing as a second early. Eyes are shallow. Flesh is white, sprouts blue, scale leaves faint blue. Foliage is of medium height and spreading. Stems branching, marked red-purple at base.

Witchhill (1881)

A long oval white maturing as a first early. Has a very smooth skin. Eyes are very shallow and on the point of tuber. Flesh is white and of waxy texture. Foliage is of medium height.

Yam (1836)

A round brick red, dented at heel, maturing as a late maincrop. Eyes are medium to deep, recessed. Eyebrows long and raised. Flesh is yellow, sprouts pink. Foliage is tall and upright. Stems branching freely, mottled red-purple, wings are waved. Leaf marked open.

Chapter X

The Case for Potash

The potato crop is highly responsive to potash and takes up more potash than any other nutrient and more than most other crops. Where potatoes are grown on medium and light textured soils which have little ability to store potash, it is important to make adequate applications of potash which will produce crops both for high yield and tuber quality. Potassium is an essential nutrient for all plants, as it is involved in the regulation of water in the plant and to retain it there. With adequate potassium crops use water much more efficiently.

Potassium is essential to get the maximum leaf expansion and stem elongation; this helps in achieving rapid ground cover by crops, so maximising collection of sunshine and thus growth rate during the critical early stages of growth. Potassium is intimately involved in the metabolism and movement of carbohydrate within plants and in potatoes, it is involved in the movement of sugars to the growing tubers for storage as starch. The potato takes up more potassium than most other plants in the six weeks after the crop emerges. The crop takes up to two-thirds of its total uptake at an average daily rate of about 6 units K_2O/acre-day. In late July, early August the potash uptake in main crop potatoes reaches its maximum. For a high yielding crop this can be as much as 350 units/acre. As the tops die back some potash returns to the soil and by harvest more than three quarters of the maximum uptake is found in the tubers. At lifting, about 11.5 units of potash requirement for high yielding crops, big eg/acre crop=288 units K_2O offtake. Shortage of potash leads to thinner cell walls and less lignification and consequently reduced resistance to disease and weakness in stems.

Potato crop yield is reduced by mild potash deficiency without any visual symptoms showing. In cases of severe deficiency, growth is much reduced and the leaf canopy may not close between the rows. Leaf margins, especially on older leaves become brown and leaves die prematurely. It has been demonstrated in many experiments that high potash fertilisers increase tuber size and give a higher proportion of ware compared to seed as potash rates are increased. To some extent the increased tuber size is due to high concentration of K in the soil, damaging roots and reducing tuber numbers for many growers. This is probably beneficial, but for seed production, where the object is to produce a maximum of smaller tubers, it is advantageous to use sulphate of potash which reduces the effect on size. Most potato trial results show that increasing rates of potash application reduces tuber dry matter content by up to approximately 2% it should be noted that high nitrogen applications have also been observed to have a similar effect.

There is evidence to suggest that the use of potassium chloride (muriate) can reduce DM (dry matter) of potato. Sulphate of potash has shown to improve dry matter of potatoes which may be critical to achieving the minimum level of DM, though other cultural practices such as irrigation management may be more important.

The potato crop with its relatively poor rating system, high soil nutrient status is vital. Long term experiments have shown that it takes a long time to rebuild potato yields once the soil potash status has been run down. Taking into account the large amounts of potash removed by the potato crop and the need to maintain soil potash status, potash application is still recommended even with high soil potash status. In view of the high value of the response of potatoes to potash and the benefit of maintaining high soil fertility, it is sound practice to fertilise this crop generously and utilise the residual fertiliser value for the following crop. Potatoes are not highly responsive to magnesium applications unless the soil Mg index is under 1. However, bearing in mind the tendency for high levels of potash to depress magnesium uptake, where high yields are grown, an application of magnesium fertiliser should be considered if the soil Mg index is under 2. Foliar methods are not appropriate to the application of potash as it is not possible for the potato plant to take up the large amounts required through the leaves.

The potato crop is very sensitive to moisture stress so that in dry seasons unirrigated crop yields can be as much as half that of wet seasons. For this reason, on light textured soils and in dry areas, irrigation is well worth the effort. For potato crops, carefully controlled irrigation should increase the uptake of nutrients from the soil. Although there might be a possibility of heavy rainfall after irrigation, causing leaching, this is unlikely to be important where the irrigation

is done carefully in relation to soil moisture deficit. On balance, therefore where crops are irrigated, higher yields will require increased potash application rates to balance crop removal of potash.

MAGNESIUM

Magnesium deficiency can be a very common problem especially in wet seasons, for potato growing in light soils. The tissue between the veins on mature leaves first turns yellow then brown and becomes brittle and growth may become stunted. Affected plants should be sprayed at first sign of trouble with $1/2$ lb of Magnesium Sulphate in $2 1/2$ gallons of water and repeated once or twice at fourteen day intervals to improve the crop.

COOKING DISCOLOURATION

Blackening of the flesh commonly occurs after cooking. Many potato varieties are susceptible to blackening and some have good resistance. However, if blackening occurs before cooking the trouble is usually due to a deficiency of potash during the growing season, or storing potatoes at too high a temperature, especially in unventilated bags such as paper bags for too long. In early days it was thought that too much artificial fertiliser was the main cause of after-cooking blackening. This does not contribute to the problem.

Chapter XI

The Five Main Soil Types

LOAM

A loamy soil is the ideal blend of clay and sand. It has the advantage of the two types and none of their disadvantages. The presence of the sand allows the water to percolate through quickly and the presence of the clay helps to keep the soil moist. A loamy soil is sufficiently warm and is not so lacking in plant food as sand. Of course loams differ in accordance with the proportion of sand that is present. Like most other soils a dressing of lime can be an advantage (but not for potato crops) and it will certainly require regular applications of well rotted farmyard manure or compost to keep the soil in good fertile condition.

CLAY

This is a smooth silky soil to touch which can be rubbed through one's fingernails without feeling gritty. Even when well drained it is inclined to be wet and can be rather difficult to cultivate during rainy periods. Clay soils are best dug in the autumn or very early winter and left rough. The winter rains and frosts will help to break down the exposed lumps of soil and so make them more workable in the spring. If worked in extremely wet conditions clay soil has a habit of setting like cement and is then rather difficult to work and break down afterwards.

HEAVY

Clay soils are recognised as cropping late because they are cold and take a long time to warm up in the spring. It is impossible to work them as early in the spring as in the case of sandy loam soils. Clay soils on the other hand are richer in plant food than sands, and in a dry summer season are valuable because of their water-retention.

SANDY

A sandy soil is light and free, it is easy to cultivate and can be forked or hoed at most times. It is called a warm soil because it accepts the sun's rays much more quickly in the spring and so can be put into production earlier than heavy soils. Sandy soils are however low in plant foods and especially potash which is essential to the potato crop and they do not retain moisture easily. Contrary to popular belief they can be very acid and so require regular applications of lime. They are invariably short of organic matter and larger amounts of well rotted dung or compost should be added each season than in the case of clay soils. If the humus content is to be kept up in this way such soils can be encouraged to hold the moisture much better. Lime applications are not recommended for potato crops.

PEATY SOILS

In some parts of the country peaty soils are described as mosslands. They often become waterlogged and so require careful draining and as they are usually very acid or sour, lime has to be added. Their one great advantage is that there is plenty of organic matter present and little compost needs to be added. The brown peat lands are much easier to work and crop than the black heavy bog-like peats. There is very little plant food in peat, so additional fertilisers should be incorporated for potato growing.

LIMEY SOILS

A chalky or limey soil is usually rather shallow. It is lacking in humus and unfortunately in plant foods; such soils are dry, sticky and unpleasant to cultivate when wet. It is equally disappointing in dry seasons because it suffers so soon from lack of water. Plants growing in such soils often suffer from lime-induced chlorosis which is reflected in yellow leaves and stunted growth. Chalky soils have one advantage, which is that they are not acid, and so it is seldom, if ever, necessary to lime them. Much can be done with them if vast quantities of organic matter are applied to the surface of the soil each season in early winter. Limey soils are not highly recommended for growing potatoes.

Chapter XII

List of Potato Varieties

WHITE VARIETIES

A

ABERDEEN FAVOURITE	E.M.	G.B|	1921	Round
ACCENT	F.E.	N.L.	1989	Round Oval
ACHIEVEMENT	E.M.	G.B.	1922	Oval
ACKERSEGEN	E.M.	D.	1929	Round Oval
ACREMA	E.M.	N.L.	1985	Round
ACREMA	E.M.	N.L.	1985	Oval
ACQUISITION	S.E	G.B.	1911	Round
ALNWICK CASTLE	F.E.	G.B.	1920	Oval
ADORA	F.E.	N.L.	1989	Long Oval
ADRETTA	S.E.	D.D.R.	1975	Round Oval
AGRI	E.M.	D.	1985	Long Oval
AILSA	E.M.	G.B.	1984	Round Oval
ALANNAH	E.M.	I.R.L.	1929	Round Oval
ALBERTA	S.E.	N.L.	1934	Long Oval
ALBION	E.M.	N.L.	1928	Round
ALCMARIA	F.E.	N.L.	1969	Long Oval
ALLERFRUHESTE GELBE	S.E.	D.	1922	Round
ALLY	E.M.	G.B.	1915	Round Oval
AMAZONE	F.E.	N.L.	1983	Long Oval
AMEDO	E.M.	N.L.	1989	Oval
AMERICA	F.E.	U.S.A.	1876	Round
AMINCA	F.E.	N.L.	1977	Long Oval
ANNABELL	F.E.	N.L.	1974	Round Oval
APEX	E.M.	D	1988	Long Oval
APOLLONIA	S.E.	N.L.	1970	Long Oval
APTA	E.M.	D.	1951	Long Oval
AQUILA	E.M.	D.	1942	Round Oval
ARGOS	E.M.	G.B.	1995	Round
ARGYLL FAVOURITE	S.E.	G.B.	1921	Round
ARKULA	F.E.	D.D.R.	1975	Oval
ARMA	E.M.	G.B.	1986	Long Oval
ARRAN BANNER	E.M.	G.B.	1927	Round
ARRAN BARD	E.M.	G.B.	1938	Oval
ARRAN CAIRN	L.M.	G.B|	1930	Long Oval
ARRAN CHIEF	L.M.	G.B.	1911	Round

ARRAN COMET	F.E.	G.B.	1957	Oval
ARRAN COMRADE	S.E.	G.B.	1918	Round
ARRAN CONSUL	E.M.	G.B.	1925	Oval
ARRAN CREST	F.E.	G.B.	1928	Round
ARRAN PEAK	L.M.	G.B.	1935	Oval
ARRAN PILOT	F.E.	G.B.	1930	Long Oval
ARRAN SIGNET	S.E.	G.B.	1935	Long Oval
ARRAN VIKING	E.M.	G.B.	1945	Oval
AS	E.M.	N.	1930	Oval
ASPARGES	E.M.	D.K.	1872	Long
ASTARTE	L.M.	N.L.	1976	Long Oval
ATICA	F.E.	D.	1971	Long Oval
ATLANTIC	E.M.	U.S.A.	1991	Round
ATRELA	E.M.	N.L.	1983	Round Oval
AULA	E.M.	D.	1974	Oval
AUSONIA	S.E.	N.L.	1981	Oval
AVALANCHE	S.E.	G.B.	1989	Round Oval
AVENIR	E.M.	N.L.	1957	Long Oval
AVONDALE	L.M.	I.R.L.	1982	Round Oval

B

B.F.15	S.E.	F.	1947	Long
BAILLIE	S.E.	G.B.	1981	Round Oval
BALLYDOON	F.E.	G.B.	1931	Oval
BALMORAL CASTLE	L.M.	G.B.	1912	Round
BALVAIRD	S.E.	G.B.	1926	Oval
BARLEY BOUNTY	E.M.	G.B.	1905	Long Oval
BARAKA	L.M.	N.L.	1971	Oval
BARIMA	F.E.	N.L.	1953	Round
BELLAHOUSTON	L.M.	G.B.	1940	Round
BENALT	E.M.	G.B.	1900	Round
BEN CRUACHAN	L.M.	G.B.	1923	Oval
BEN LOMOND	S.E.	G.B.	1923	Oval
BENOL	E.M.	N.L.	1984	Round Oval
BERBER	S.E.	N.L.	1983	Oval
BEROLINA	S.E.	D.	1977	Oval
BERWICK CASTLE	S.E.	G.B.	1917	Round
BINJE	E.M.	N.L.	1910	Long Oval
BISHOP	L.M.	G.B.	1912	Long Oval
BLACK CASTLE	E.M.	G.B.	1964	Long Oval
BLACK KNIGHT	E.M.	G.B.	1964	Long Oval
BLANKA	S.E.	N.L.	1970	Long Oval
BLUE GLOSS	E.M.	G.B.	1924	Round

BLUE GREY	L.M.	G.B.	1924	Round
BOBBIE BURNS	E.M.	G.B.	1915	Round
BOREAS	E.M.	N.L.	1980	Oval
BORKA	E.M.	C.S.	1986	Round
BRIGHT	S.E.	N.L.	1988	Oval
BRIO	E.M.	N.L.	1972	Round Oval
BRITISH QUEEN	S.E.	G.B.	1894	Oval
BRITTA	S.E.	D.	1980	Oval
BUCHAN	E.M.	G.B.	1993	Round Oval

C

CANOGA	E.M.	U.S.A.	1950	Round
CARINA	F.E.	N.L.	1971	Round Oval
CARISBROOKE CASTLE	F.E.	G.B.	1914	Kidney
CARLINGFORD	S.E.	G.B.	1982	Round Oval
CAXTON	E.M.	G.B.	1986	Oval
CELURCA	L.M.	G.B.	1896	Oval
CELT	L.M.	G.B.	1920	Oval
CENTENARY	S.E.	G.B.	1900	Round
CHAMPION	L.M.	G.B.	1876	Round
CHANCELLOR	F.E.	G.B.	1952	Long Oval
CHARLOTTE	S.E.	F.	1981	Long Oval
CHARLY	F.E.	F.	1988	Long Oval
CHIPPEWA	S.E.	U.S.A.	1933	Round Oval
CHRISTA	F.E.	D.	1975	Long Oval
CHURCHILL	F.E.	G.B.	1950	Round Oval
CIVA	F.E.	N.L.	1960	Oval
CLADA	L.M.	I.R.L.	1973	Round Oval
CLAN DONNACHIE	F.E.	G.B.	1960	Oval
CLARISSA	E.M.	D.	1984	Long Oval
CLAUDIA	E.M.	F.	1955	Long Oval
CLAYMORE	L.M.	G.B.	1927	Round
CLIMAX	S.E.	N.L.	1955	Oval
COLLEEN	F.E.	I.R.L.	1993	Round Oval
COLMO	F.E.	N.L.	1973	Round Oval
COLOURLESS	E.M.	G.B.	1891	Round
COMLE	L.M.	S.	1982	Long Oval
CONCORDE	F.E.	N.L.	1988	Long Oval
CONCURRENT	F.E.	N.L.	1985	Long Oval
CONFERENCE	E.M.	G.B.	1948	Oval
CONQUEST	S.E.	G.B.	1912	Round Oval
CONTESSA	F.E.	N.L.	1981	Long Oval
CORINE	F.E.	N.L.	1976	Round Oval

COSTELLA	S.E.	N.L.	1984	Oval
CRAIGS ALLIANCE	F.E.	G.B.	1948	Oval
CRAIGS BOUNTY	L.M.	G.B.	1946	Long Oval
CRAIGS DEFIANCE	E.M.	G.B.	1938	Long Oval
CRAIGS SNOW WHITE	L.M.	G.B.	1947	Long Oval
CROFT	E.M.	G.B.	1975	Oval
CROMWELL	E.M.	G.B.	1985	Round Oval
CRUSADER	S.E.	G.B.	1918	Long Oval
CULPA	E.M.	D.	1974	Oval
CUMNOCK	S.E.	G.B.	1930	Oval

D

DALBY SPECIAL	S.E.	G.B.	1963	Long Oval
DATURA	L.M.	D.	1957	Oval
DANVA	L.M.	D.K.	1982	Round
DARGILL EARLY	S.E.	G.B.	1917	Long Oval
DARWINA	E.M.	N.L.	1981	Long Oval
DEAN (WILSON)	L.M.	G.B.	1922	Round Oval
DIAMANT	E.M.	N.L.	1982	Long Oval
DISCOVERY	L.M.	G.B.	1903	Round
DEODARA	E.M.	D.	1913	Round Oval
DOBBIES ASSET	E.M.	G.B.	1934	Round Oval
DOMINA	E.M.	D.	1982	Oval
DOMINION	L.M.	G.B.	1916	Round Oval
DONATA	S.E.	N.L.	1965	Oval
DOON ARCHER	L.M.	G.B.	1936	Long Oval
DOON BOUNTY	S.E.	G.B.	1939	Oval
DOON EARLY	F.E.	G.B.	1934	Round Oval
DOON PEARL	E.M.	G.B.	1931	Round
DOON STAR	L.M.	G.B.	1926	Oval
DR MCINTOSH	E.M.	G.B.	1944	Long Oval
DRAGO	S.E.	N.L.	1970	Round
DRUMMOND CASTLE	E.M.	G.B.	1917	Long Oval
DUKE OF KENT	L.M.	G.B.	1935	Round
DUKE OF YORK	F.E.	G.B.	1891	Round Oval
DUNBAR ROVER	S.E.	G.B.	1936	Oval
DUNBAR STANDARD	L.M.	G.B.	1936	Long Oval
DUNBAR YEOMAN	F.E.	G.B.	1932	Long Oval
DUNDROD	F.E.	G.B.	1987	Round Oval
DUNDRUM	S.E.	G.B.	1983	Round Oval
DUNLUCE	F.E.	G.B.	1976	Oval
DUNNOTTAR CASTLE	F.E.	G.B.	1915	Oval
DUNVEGAN CASTLE	F.E.	G.B.	1922	Round

E

EARLY MARKET	E.M.	G.B.	1884	Oval
EARLY BORDER	F.E.	G.B.	1882	Round
EBA	E.M.	N.L.	1966	Oval
ECLIPSE	F.E	G.B.	1900	Oval
EDINBURGH CASTLE	S.E.	G.B.	1913	Oval
EDZINA	S.E.	N.L.	1974	Long Oval
EIGENHEIMER	S.E.	N.L.	1893	Oval
ENTENTE CORDIALE	S.E.	G.B.	1917	Oval
EPICURE	F.E.	G.B.	1897	Round
ERNTESTOLZ	S.E.	D.	1976	Round Oval
ESCORT	E.M.	N.L.	1981	Oval
ESPERANTE	S.E.	N.L.	1988	Oval
ESSEX	S.E.	U.S.A.	1947	Round
ESTIMA	S.E.	N.L.	1973	Oval
ETOILE DU LEON	S.E.	F.	1935	Long Oval
EUREKA	S.E.	F.	1976	Long Oval
EVERGOOD	E.M.	G.B.	1899	Oval
EVELIN	E.M.	N.L.	1988	Long Oval
EVITA	S.E.	D.	1990	Oval
EXODUS	E.M.	N.L.	1970	Long Oval

F

FALKE	E.M.	D.	1943	Long Oval
FAMBO	S.E.	N.L.	1985	Long Oval
FAMOSA	E.M.	N.L.	1977	Oval
FANETTE	F.E.	F.	1984	Long Oval
FATIMA	E.M.	D.	1970	Round Oval
FAVOURITE	S.E.	G.B.	1883	Round
FIANNA	E.M.	N.L.	1987	Oval
FIELD MARSHALL	L.M.	G.B.	1924	Oval
FIELD ASHLEAF	F.E.	G.B.	1881	Kidney
FIFTYFOLD	S.E.	G.B.	1882	Oval
FILLBASKET	F.E.	G.B.	1881	Round
FIRST AND BEST	F.E.	G.B.	1882	Round
FOREMOST	F.E.	G.B.	1954	Round Oval
FOX	S.E.	D.	1981	Oval
FRESCO	F.E.	N.L.	1985	Round Oval
FRISO	F.E.	N.L.	1930	Round Oval
FRONIKA	S.E.	N.L.	1985	Round Oval
FRUHMOLLE	F.E.	D.	1931	Long Oval

G

GABI	E.M.	D.	1970	Long Oval
GENERAL	L.M.	G.B.	1901	Round
GIGANT	E.M.	N.L.	1987	Oval
GILFORD	E.M.	G.B.	1987	Long Oval
GIPSY	S.E.	F.	1984	Long Oval
GLASGOW FAVOURITE	L.M.	G.B.	1921	Round Oval
GLADIATOR	F.E.	G.B.	1906	Kidney
GLENALMOND	E.M.	G.B.	1925	Round Oval
GLEN CLOVA	L.M.	G.B.	1952	Oval
GLENESK	E.M.	G.B.	1956	Long Oval
GLENSHEE	L.M.	G.B.	1929	Oval
GLENIFFER	F.E.	G.B.	1937	Long Oval
GOLDEN WONDER	L.M.	G.B.	1904	Long Oval
GORDON CASTLE	S.E.	G.B.	1916	Round
GRANDIA	E.M.	N.L.	1973	Long Oval
GRANDIFOLIA	E.M.	D.	1973	Oval
GRANOLA	E.M.	D.	1975	Round Oval
GREAT SCOT	E.M.	G.B.	1909	Round

H

HARMONY	E.M.	G.B.	1923	Oval
HARBINGER	F.E.	G.B.	1894	Round
HARLECH CASTLE	S.E.	G.B.	1919	Kidney
HASSIA	E.M.	D.	1962	Round
HERALD	F.E.	G.B.	1928	Oval
HOME GUARD	F.E.	G.B.	1942	Round Oval
HOUMA	E.M.	U.S.A.	1936	Round Oval
HUMALDA	S.E.	N.L.	1965	Oval
HUNTER'S GOLD	S.E.	G.B.	1962	Oval
HYDRA	E.M.	D.	1969	Round Oval

I

IIONA	S.E.	D.	1976	Oval
IISE	E.M.	D.	1980	Oval
IMMUNE ASHLEAF	F.E.	D.	1891	Long Oval
INCASTAR	L.M.	N.L.	1987	Round Oval
INCOMER	L.M.	G.B.	1923	Round Oval
INGA	S.E.	N.L.	1930	Oval
INTERNATIONAL KIDNEY	E.M.	G.B.	1879	Long Oval
INTOCK	E.M.	G.B.	1970	Oval
INVERNESS FAVOURITE	L.M.	G.B.	1921	Long Oval
INVINCIBLE	L.M.	G.B.	1898	Round

IRIS	E.M.	N.L.	1936	Round
IRISH CHIEFTAIN	L.M.	I.R.L.	1916	Oval
IRISH PEACE	F.E.	G.B.	1973	Round Oval
IRISH WHITES	L.M.	I.R.L.	1921	Long Oval
ISIS	L.M.	G.B.	1914	Round
ISOLA	E.M.	D.	1958	Oval
IWA	E.M.	N.Z.L.	1978	Oval

J

JAERIA	S.E.	N.L.	1969	Long Oval
JAUNE DE HOLLAND	S.E.	N.L.	1907	Long Oval
JEWEL	E.M.	N.L.	1985	Round Oval
JULIVER	E.M.	D.	1976	Oval

K

KARIN	E.M.	C.S.	1980	Long Oval
KARLENA	F.E.	N.L.	1993	Round Oval
KATAHDIN	E.M.	U.S.A.	1932	Round
KELTIA	S.E.	F.	1964	Long Oval
KENNEBEC	E.M.	U.S.A.	1948	Round Oval
KEREBEL	S.E.	F.	1961	Long Oval
KER PONDY	E.M.	F.	1949	Long Oval
KESWICK	S.E.	C.D.N.	1951	Round Oval
KING GEORGE V	S.E.	G.B.	1911	Long Oval
KINGSTON	L.M.	G.B.	1981	Oval
KIPFLER	S.E.	A.	1955	Long
KIRSTY	E.M.	G.B.	1982	Round Oval
KISMET	F.E.	G.B.	1986	Round Oval
KLONDYKE	E.M.	N.L.	1978	Long Oval
KORRIGANE	E.M.	F.	1982	Oval
KROLISA	S.E.	N.L.	1989	Long Oval
KROMARGRETHA	E.M.	N.L.	1986	Oval
KURREL	E.M.	A.U.S.	1966	Round

L

LADY TRUSCOTT	L.M.	G.B.	1883	Round
LAJANA	E.M.	D.	1982	Oval
LAMIA	S.E.	F.	1981	Long Oval
LANGWORTHY	L.M.	G.B.	1876	Long Oval
LEINSTER WONDER	L.M.	I.R.L.	1910	Round
LIBERTAS	E.M.	N.L.	1946	Round
LIDO	E.M.	N.L.	1988	Oval
LINDSEY	E.M.	G.B.	1986	Round Oval

LINZER DELIKATESS	S.E.	A.	1976	Long Oval
LISA	E.M.	A.	1976	Round Oval
LISETA	S.E.	N.L.	1988	Long Oval
LOLA	S.E.	F.	1981	Long Oval
LONG LEAF	E.M.	G.B.	1952	Round Oval
LORD SCONE	S.E.	G.B.	1925	Long Oval
LUMPERS	E.M.	I.R.L.	1806	Long Oval
LUTETIA	F.E.	N.L.	1988	Oval
LYMM GRAY	S.E.	G.B.	1903	Round

M

MACBETH'S CASTLE	S.E.	G.B.	1924	Oval
MADAM	F.E.	N.L.	1980	Oval
MAGALI	S.E.	N.L.	1988	Long Oval
MAGNA	E.M.	N.L.	1989	Round Oval
MAGNET	S.E.	G.B.	1883	Kidney
MAGNIFICENT	E.M.	G.B.	1918	Oval
MAGNUM BONUM	L.M.	G.B.	1876	Long Oval
MAINS TRIUMPH	L.M.	G.B.	1923	Oval
MAJESTIC	E.M.	G.B.	1911	Long Oval
MANNA	F.E.	N.L.	1975	Long Oval
MANSOUR	E.M.	N.L.	1987	Oval
MARCONI	L.M.	G.B.	1927	Round Oval
MARFONA	S.E.	N.L.	1975	Round Oval
MARIA	F.E.	S.	1972	Oval
MARIANA	F.E.	F.	1982	Oval
MARIS ANCHOR	F.E.	G.B.	1971	Oval
MARIS BARD	F.E.	G.B.	1972	Long Oval
MARIS PAGE	S.E.	G.B.	1966	Long Oval
MARIS PEER	S.E.	G.B.	1962	Oval
MARIS PIPER	E.M.	G.B.	1964	Oval
MARITTA	L.M.	D.	1947	Round
MASTERPIECE	L.M.	G.B.	1887	Round
MATCHLESS	S.E.	G.B.	1889	Round
MAY QUEEN	F.E.	G.B.	1900	Long Oval
MELISSA	E.M.	F.	1988	Long Oval
MIGHTY ATOM	E.M.	G.B.	1911	Oval
MILLARS BEAUTY	E.M.	G.B.	1902	Oval
MINEA	F.E.	G.B.	1963	Oval
MINERVA	F.E.	N.L.	1988	Oval
MINSAND	L.M.	D.K.	1981	Round Oval
MINSTER	E.M.	G.B.	1988	Long Oval
MIRKA	E.M.	C.S.	1955	Long Oval

MISTRAL	S.E.	F.	1985	Long Oval
MIZEN	E.M.	I.R.L.	1979	Oval
MOIRA	F.E.	G.B.	1984	Oval
MONALISA	S.E.	N.L.	1982	Long Oval
MONDIAL	E.M.	N.L.	1987	Long Oval
MONI	L.M.	D.	1972	Oval
MONIKA	E.M.	D.	1943	Round Oval
MONITOR	E.M.	N.L.	1970	Oval
MONONA	S.E.	U.S.A	1964	Round Oval
MORAG	E.M.	G.B.	1985	Round Oval
MORENE	E.M.	N.L.	1983	Long Oval
MORNA	F.E.	G.B.	1986	Round Oval
MULTA	E.M.	N.L.	1964	Oval
MYATT'S ASHLEAF	S.E.	G.B.	1847	Long Oval

N

NADINE	S.E.	G.B.	1987	Round Oval
NAVAN	L.M.	G.B.	1987	Oval
NE PLUS ULTRA	S.E..	G.B.	1897	Round
NICOLA	E.M.	D.	1973	Long Oval
NIETA	E.M.	G.B.	1986	Oval
NINETYFOLD	F.E.	G.B.	1897	Long Oval
NITHSDALE	E.M.	G.B.	1916	Long Oval
NORNA	S.E.	G.B.	1909	Oval
NONESUCH	S.E.	G.B.	1889	Round

O

OBELIX	E.M.	N.L.	1988	Oval
OLINDA	F.E.	N.L.	1980	Oval
OMBRA	F.E.	N.L.	1981	Long Oval
ONTARIO	E.M.	U.S.A.	1946	Round Oval
ORIGO	F.E.	N.L.	1987	Long Oval
ORION (N.L.)	E.M.	N.L.	1943	Round
ORION (G.B.)	E.M.	G.B.	1947	Round Oval
ORNAMENT	F.E.	N.L.	1983	Oval
OSTARA	F.E.	N.L.	1984	Oval

P

PANDA	E.M.	D.	1986	Oval
PANSTA	E.M.	N.L.	1977	Round
PARAGON	E.M.	N.L.	1976	Oval
PARNASSIA	E.M.	D.	1913	Round Oval
PATRONES	E.M.	N.L.	1959	Oval

PAWNEE	E.M.	U.S.A.	1942	Round Oval
PENTLAND ACE	S.E.	G.B.	1955	Long Oval
PENTLAND CROWN	E.M.	G.B.	1959	Oval
PENTLAND DELL	E.M.	G.B.	1961	Long Oval
PENTLAND ENVOY	F.E.	G.B.	1962	Long Oval
PENTLAND FALCON	E.M.	G.B.	1964	Long Oval
PENTLAND GLORY	F.E.	G.B.	1963	Long Oval
PENTLAND HAWK	E.M.	G.B.	1966	Long Oval
PENTLAND IVORY	E.M.	G.B.	1966	Long Oval
PENTLAND JAVELIN	F.E.	G.B.	1968	Round Oval
PENTLAND KAPPA	S.E.	G.B.	1968	Oval
PENTLAND MARBLE	F.E.	G.B.	1970	Round Oval
PENTLAND METEOR	F.E.	G.B.	1970	Oval
PENTLAND RAVEN	E.M.	G.B.	1970	Round Oval
PENTLAND SQUIRE	E.M.	G.B.	1970	Round Oval
PEPO	E.M.	D.	1919	Long Oval
PERTH FAVOURITE	L.M.	G.B.	1926	Round
PERFECTION	S.E.	G.B.	1892	Kidney
PICADOR	E.M.	G.B.	1988	Oval
PLANTA	S.E.	D.	1984	Long Oval
PODZOLA	E.M.	N.L.	1983	Oval
POMPADOUR	E.M.	N.L.	1976	Round Oval
PREMIERE	F.E.	N.L.	1979	Round Oval
PRESIDENT	L.M.	N.L.	1901	Round
PRIMADONNA	E.M.	F.	1987	Round Oval
PRIMURA	F.E.	N.L.	1963	Oval
PRIOR	F.E.	N.L.	1987	Long Oval
PROCURA	E.M.	N.L.	1971	Round Oval
PROMESSE	E.M.	N.L.	1983	Round Oval
PROMINENT	E.M.	N.L.	1968	Long Oval
PROTON	E.M.	N.L.	1975	Round Oval
PROVOST	F.E.	G.B.	1981	Round
PURITAN	F.E.	U.S.A.	1895	Oval

Q

QUEEN OF THE SOUTH	L.M.	G.B.	1947	Long Oval

R

RANGER	E.M.	G.B.	1930	Round Oval
REAAL	E.M.	N.L.	1957	Round Oval
READING ABBEY	S.E.	G.B.	1880	Oval
READING HERO	L.M.	G.B.	1881	Round
RECORD	E.M.	N.L.	1932	Round Oval

RED FIFE	E.M.	G.B.	1946	Round Oval
REGALE	E.M.	F.	1957	Long Oval
REGENT	S.E.	D.	1919	Round Oval
REGIMENT	E.M.	G.B.	1971	Round Oval
RELIANCE	L.M.	G.B.	1897	Kidney
RENOVA	E.M.	N.L.	1971	Oval
RESPONSE	E.M.	G.B.	1926	Oval
REVELINO	F.E.	N.L.	1979	Round Oval
REX	E.M.	D.	1985	Round Oval
RHODERICK DHU	L.M.	G.B.	1919	Round
RHONA	E.M.	G.B.	1984	Round Oval
RINGLEADER	F.E.	G.B.	1884	Kidney
ROCKET	F.E.	G.B.	1987	Round
ROCKS	L.M.	G.B.	1856	Round
ROSLIN CASTLE	E.M.	G.B.	1966	Round
ROSLIN CHANIA	L.M.	G.B.	1961	Long Oval
ROSLIN EBURU	L.M.	G.B.	1961	Round Oval
ROSLIN ELMENTITA	E.M.	G.B.	1961	Oval
ROSLIN MOUNT KENYA	E.M.	G.B.	1961	Oval
ROSLIN RIVIERA	E.M.	G.B.	1961	Oval
ROSLIN SASUMUA	L.M.	G.B.	1961	Long Oval
ROYAL KIDNEY	S.E.	G.B.	1899	Long Oval
RUA	E.M.	N.Z.L.	1960	Round
RURAL NEW YORKER	E.M.	U.S.A.	1888	Round Oval
RUSSET BURBANK	L.M.	U.S.A.	1880	Long Oval
RUSSET CONFERENCE	E.M.	G.B.	1958	Oval
RUSSET FORTYFOLD	E.M.	G.B.	1919	Round

S

SABINA	E.M.	S.	1977	Long Oval
SACO	E.M.	U.S.A.	1954	Round
SAMBA	E.M.	F.	1989	Long Oval
SANDRA	E.M.	D.	1985	Round Oval
SANTE	E.M.	N.L.	1983	Round Oval
SAPHIR	E.M.	D.	1960	Round Oval
SARKA	S.E.	G.B.	1985	Long Oval
SASKIA	F.E.	N.L.	1946	Oval
SATISFACTION	E.M.	G.B.	1889	Oval
SATISFACTION	L.M.	G.B.	1887	Oval
SATURNA	E.M.	N.L.	1964	Round Oval
SAVA	S.E.	D.K.	1981	Round Oval
SAXON	S.E.	G.B.	1992	Long Oval
SCHOOLMASTER	L.M.	G.B.	1876	Round

SCOTSTON SUPREME	E.M.	G.B.	1959	Long Oval
SCOTTISH CHIEF	E.M.	G.B.	1901	Round
SEAFORDE	E.M.	G.B.	1987	Oval
SEBAGO	E.M.	U.S.A.	1938	Round Oval
SEFTON WONDER	E.M.	G.B.	1925	Round
SEMENA	F.E.	D.	1982	Long Oval
SEQUOIA	L.M.	U.S.A.	1939	Round
SHARPE'S EXPRESS	F.E.	G.B.	1900	Long Oval
SHARPE'S VICTOR	F.E.	G.B.	1891	Oval
SHEPODY	E.M.	C.D.N.	1980	Long Oval
SHERIFF	E.M.	G.B.	1981	Round Oval
SHERINE	S.E.	G.B.	1987	Oval
SIEGLINDE	S.E.	D.	1935	Long Oval
SIENTJE	E.M.	N.L.	1951	Long Oval
SIERRA	E.M.	G.B.	1992	Long Oval
SIRCO	F.E.	N.L.	1976	Round Oval
SIRTEMA	F.E.	N.L.	1951	Round Oval
SOUTHESK	L.M.	G.B.	1925	Round
SPARTAN	E.M.	N.L.	1963	Oval
SPERRIN	S.E.	G.B.	1988	Long Oval
SPRY'S ABUNDANCE	E.M.	G.B.	1923	Round Oval
SPUNTA	S.E.	N.L.	1968	Long Oval
STAMINA	E.M.	G.B.	1990	Long Oval
STINA	E.M.	S.	1976	Round Oval
STIRLING CASTLE	E.M.	G.B.	1914	Oval
STORMONT DAWN	E.M.	G.B.	1942	Round Oval
STORMONT ENTERPRISE	E.M.	G.B.	1969	Oval
STORMONT STAR	E.M.	G.B.	1945	Long Oval
STRATH	E.M.	G.B.	1979	Round Oval
SUMMIT	L.M.	G.B.	1912	Oval
SUPREME	S.E.	G.B.	1893	Kidney
SUPERLATIVE	L.M.	G.B.	1905	Kidney
SUTTON'S ASHLEAF	F.E.	G.B.	1876	Kidney
SUTTON'S ABUNDANCE	E.M.	G.B.	1886	Round Oval
SUTTON'S ANGUS GEM	E.M.	G.B.	1956	Round Oval
SUTTON'S COMMANDER	E.M.	G.B.	1928	Oval
SUTTON'S E. REGENT	S.E.	G.B.	1882	Round
SUTTON'S PREFERENCE	S.E.	G.B.	1960	Long Oval
SUTTON'S SEEDLING	S.E.	G.B.	1886	Oval
SVATAVA	E.M.	C.S.	1983	Round Oval
SWIFT	F.E.	G.B.	1993	Round Oval

T

TAHI	E.M.	N.Z.L.	1960	Round Oval
TAIGA	L.M.	D.	1973	Round Oval
TARAGO	E.M.	A.U.S.	1983	Round Oval
TAYSIDE	F.E.	G.B.	1952	Long Oval
TEENA	E.M.	G.B.	1986	Round
TELLA	S.E.	D.	1981	Oval
TEMPLAR	L.M.	G.B.	1912	Round Oval
THE ALNESS	S.E.	G.B.	1934	Oval
THE BARON	S.E.	G.B.	1928	Long Oval
THE MAC	E.M.	G.B.	1901	Oval
THE MASSIE	S.E.	G.B.	1906	Round
THOMANA	E.M.	D.	1977	Oval
THYNIA	E.M.	N.L.	1964	Round Oval
TIMATE	S.E.	N.L.	1989	Long Oval
TINWALD PERFECTION	E.M.	G.B.	1914	Oval
TITANA	F.E.	D.	1978	Oval
TOLEDO	E.M.	G.B.	1988	Round Oval
TONDRA	E.M.	D.	1960	Round Oval
TORRIDON	E.M.	G.B.	1988	Long Oval
TRIUMPH	L.M.	G.B.	1892	Oval
TUSKAR	F.E	I.R.L.	1978	Round Oval

U

UKAMA	F.E.	N.L.	1977	Long Oval
ULSTER BEACON	E.M.	G.B.	1954	Long Oval
ULSTER CHIEFTAIN	F.E.	G.B.	1938	Long Oval
ULSTER COMMERCE	E.M.	G.B.	1945	Round
ULSTER CONCORD	E.M.	G.B.	1968	Oval
ULSTER CROMLECH	E.M.	G.B.	1943	Round Oval
ULSTER DALE	S.E.	G.B.	1950	Oval
ULSTER EARL	E.M.	G.B.	1943	Long Oval
ULSTER EMBLEM	S.E.	G.B.	1948	Long Oval
ULSTER GLADE	E.M.	G.B.	1962	Long Oval
ULSTER GLEN	E.M.	G.B.	1958	Oval
ULSTER GOZO	E.M.	G.B.	1954	Oval
ULSTER KNIGHT	E.M.	G.B.	1953	Oval
ULSTER LEADER	E.M.	G.B.	1947	Long Oval
ULSTER MAGNET	F.E.	G.B.	1960	Oval
ULSTER MALTA	E.M.	G.B.	1955	Round Oval
ULSTER MONARCH	S.E.	G.B.	1937	Long Oval
ULSTER PRINCE	F.E.	G.B.	1947	Long Oval
ULSTER RANGER	E.M.	G.B.	1958	Long Oval

ULSTER SCEPTRE	F.E.	G.B.	1963	Long Oval
ULSTER SUPREME	L.M.	G.B.	1946	Oval
ULSTER TORCH	E.M.	G.B.	1953	Long Oval
ULSTER VISCOUNT	E.M.	G.B.	1968	Oval
UNIVERS	S.E.	N.L.	1982	Long Oval
UP-TO-DATE	L.M.	G.B.	1894	Long Oval

V

VAN GOUGH	E.M.	N.L.	1989	Oval
VANGUARD	F.E.	G.B.	1939	Round Oval
VANTAGE	M.	N.L.	1983	Oval
VELOKA	E.M.	N.L.	1989	Oval
VERENA	S.E.	D.	1974	Oval
VERITAS	E.M.	N.L.	1989	Round Oval
VIOLA	F.E.	D.	1938	Long Oval
VITAL	E.M.	N.L.	1988	Long Oval
VIVAKS	S.E.	N.L.	1971	Long Oval
VULKANO	S.E.	N.L.	1984	Round Oval

W

WAREGEM	S.E.	G.B.	1989	Round Oval
WARWICK CASTLE	S.E.	G.B.	1915	Round
WEBB'S PRIDE	S.E.	G.B.	1951	Long Oval
WELSA	E.M.	A.	1978	Round Oval
WHITE CITY	L.M.	G.B.	1909	Long Oval
WHITE FORTYFOLD	E.M.	G.B.	1893	Round
WHITE KIDNEY	F.E.	G.B.	1888	Kidney
WILD ROSE	L.M.	G.B.	1901	Oval
WILJA	S.E.	N.L.	1967	Long Oval
WINDSOR	S.E.	G.B.	1995	Round Oval
WINDSOR CASTLE	S.E.	G.B.	1890	Oval
WINSTON	F.E.	G.B.	1992	Round Oval
WITCHILL	F.E.	G.B.	1881	Long Oval
WOODSTOCK KIDNEY	S.E.	G.B.	1870	Oval
WONDERFUL	E.M.	G.B.	1928	Long Oval

Y

YESMINA	E.M.	F.	1989	Long Oval

SPORTS

BLUE CATRIONA	Sport of Catriona
PART COLOURED ARRAN VICTORY	Sport of Arran Victory
PART COLOURED BUTE BLUES	Sport of Bute Blues
PINK DUKE OF YORK	Sport of Duke of York
RED CARA	Sport of Cara
RED CRAIGS ROYAL	Sport of Craigs Royal
RED DRAYTON	Sport of Drayton
RED KING EDWARD	Sport of King Edward
RED PENTLAND BEAUTY	Sport of Pentland Beauty
RED PENTLAND LUSTRE	Sport of Pentland Lustre
RED ULSTER PREMIER	Sport of Ulster Premier
RED ULSTER CLASSIC	Sport of Ulster Classic

PART-COLOURED VARIETIES

Variety	Maturity	Country	Year	Shape
	A			
AFTON	L.M.	I.R.L.	1988	Round Oval
ARONIA	S.E.	D.	1954	Oval
ARRAN VICTORY	L.M.	G.B.	1927	Round Oval
	B			
BARBARA	E.M.	D.	1982	Long Oval
BEAUTY OF BUTE	E.M	G.B	1890	Round
BONTE DESIREE	E.M.	N.L.	1967	Long Oval
BRODICK	E.M.	G.B.	1990	Round Oval
BRODIE	E.M.	G.B.	1993	Long Oval
BUTE BLUES	E.M.	G.B.	1980	Long Oval
	C			
CARA	L.M.	I.R.L.	1976	Round Oval
COMMANDEUR	E.M.	N.L.	1963	Oval
CRAIGS ROYAL	S.E.	G.B.	1947	Long Oval
CULTRA	E.M.	I.R.L.	1988	Round Oval
	D			
DELTA STAR	E.M.	N.L.	1982	Long Oval
DOON CASTLE	F.E.	G.B.	1943	Oval
DOON EIRE	L.M.	G.B.	1942	Long Oval
DOON WELL	S.E.	G.B.	1943	Oval
DRAYTON	E.M.	G.B.	1976	Round Oval
DUNBAR CAVALIER	L.M.	G.B.	1930	Oval
	E			
ELVINGSTON GOWAN	L.M.	G.B.	1969	Oval
	F			
FIGARO	E.M.	G.B.	1993	Round
	G			
GLADSTONE	E.M.	G.B.	1932	Oval
GLAMIS	E.M.	G.B.	1989	Long Oval
	H			
HERAKLES	E.M.	N.L.	1931	Long Oval

J

JOHN BULL	E.M.	G.B.	1913	Round

K

KAIMES BEAUTY	E.M.	G.B.	1956	Oval
KARAMA	L.M.	G.B.	1993	Long Oval
KING EDWARD	E.M.	G.B.	1902	Long Oval
KITCHENER OF KHARTOUM	E.M.	G.B.	1920	Round Oval

L

LOCHAR	L.M.	G.B.	1915	Round

M

MARQUIS OF BUTE	S.E.	G.B.	1915	Round
MEIN'S EARLY ROUND	S.E.	G.B.	1916	Round
MERLIN	E.M.	G.B.	1993	Round Oval

N

NORTHERN STAR	L.M.	G.B.	1900	Round

P

PEACH BLOOM	L.M.	U.S.A.	1923	Round
PENTA	S.E.	N.L.	1983	Round
PENTLAND BEAUTY	F.E.	G.B.	1955	Oval
PENTLAND LUSTRE	F.E.	G.B.	1969	Long Oval
PICASSO	L.M.	N.L.	1993	Long Oval
PINKI	S.E.	D.	1985	Oval

S

SALINKA	S.E.	A.	1980	Oval
SHELAGH	E.M.	G.B.	1986	Round Oval
SHULA	E.M.	G.B.	1986	Oval
STORMONT 480	E.M.	G.B.	1959|	Oval
SUTTONS OLYMPIC	S.E.	G.B.	1954	Long Oval

U

ULSTER BREVET	E.M.	G.B.	1972	Oval
ULSTER CLASSIC	S.E.	G.B.	1967	Oval
ULSTER ENSIGN	S.E.	G.B.	1946	Long Oval
ULSTER GROVE	E.M.	G.B.	1959	Long Oval
ULSTER LANCER	E.M.	G.B.	1972	Round Oval
ULSTER PREMIER	F.E.	G.B.	1944	Long Oval

V

| VENTURA | E.M. | N.L. | 1986 | Round Oval |
| VENUS | E.M. | G.B. | 1946 | Oval |

Y

| YUKON GOLD | S.E. | C.D.N. | 1980 | Round Oval |

PINK OR RED SKINNED VARIETIES

Variety	Maturity	Country	Year	Shape
	A			
ADAMS APPLE	L.M.	G.B.	1930	Round Oval
ADIRONDACK	E.M.	U.S.A.	1881	Round
ALHAMRA	E.M.	G.B.	1986	Long Oval
ALTENA	S.E.	N.L.	1982	Long Oval
ALWARA	E.M.	D.	1985	Long Oval
AMADEUS	E.M.	N.L.	1994	Oval
AMBER	L.M.	I.R.L.	1976	Round Oval
ANTAR	L.M.	G.B.	1987	Long Oval
APACHE	E.M.	N.L.	1986	Long Oval
ARKA	E.M.	N.L.	1961	Long Oval
ARRAN ROSE	I.E.	G.B.	1919	Oval
	B			
BARTINA	E.M.	N.L.	1988	Round Oval
BLACK KING.	M.	G.B.	1961	Round
BLACK QUEEN	M.	G.B.	1974	Round
BLUSH	E.M.	G.B.	1990	Round Oval
BONNIE DUNDEE	I.E.	G.B.	1962	Round
BURMANIA	E.M.	N.L.	1957	Round
BUSTAN	L.M.	G.B.	1985	Long Oval
	C			
CARDINAL (G.B.)	E.M.	G.B.	1916	Long Oval
CARDINAL (N.L)	E.M.	N.L.	1972	Oval
CENTIFOLIA	E.M.	D.	1919	Round Oval
CHIEFTAIN	E.M.	G.B.	1993	Round Oval
CLEOPATRA	I.E.	N.L.	1980	Oval
CORONATION (1953)	E.M.	G.B.	1958	Long Oval
CRAIGNEIL	L.M.	G.B.	1935	Round

D

DELCORA	E.M.	N.L.	1988	Long Oval
DESIREE	E.M.	N.L.	1962	Long Oval
DIANA	E.M.	N.L.	1980	Oval

E

EARLY PINK CHAMPION	2E.	G.B.	1919	Round
EARLY ROSE	F.E.	U.S.A.	1861	Long Oval
EROICA	E.M.	D.	1975	Oval
ETOILE DU NORD	E.M.	F.	1909	Round Oval

F

FLAMENCO	E.M.	N.L.	1985	Long Oval
FLAMINIA	E.M.	F.	1958	Oval
FLOURBALL	E.M.	G.B.	1895	Round
FOULA RED	L.M.	G.B.	1951	Round
FOXTON	E.M.	G.B.	1981	Oval
FRONTIER	E.M.	G.B.	1988	Long Oval
FURORE	E.M.	N.L.	1930	Round Oval

G

GINEKE	E.M.	N.L.	1950	Round Oval
GRACIA	E.	N.L.	1979	Long Oval
GRAMPIAN	S.E.	G.B.	1971	Round
GREGOR CUPS	L.M.	G.B.	1903	Round

I

IRENE	E.M.	N.L.	1953	Round
IRISH QUEEN	L.M.	G.B.	1910	Round

J

JANET	E.M.	N.L.	1984	Round Oval

K

KENZY	L.M.	G.B.	1987	Oval
KERR'S PINK	L.M.	G.B.	1917	Round
KIMBERLEY	E.M.	N.L.	1989	Round Oval
KONDOR	E.M.	N.L.	1984	Long Oval
KONING	E.M.	N.L.	1966	Oval

L

LADY ROSETTA	S.E.	N.L.	1988	Round
LIRO	E.M.	A.	1981	Long Oval
LORD ROSEBERY	S.E.	G.B.	1920	Round

LIST OF POTATO VARIETIES

M

MAUD MEG	L.M.	G.B.	1921	Long Oval
MAXINE	E.M.	G.B.	1993	Round Oval
MONTANA	E.M.	D.	1971	Oval
MR BRESEE	S.E.	U.S.A.	1870	Long Oval

O

OREB	E.M.	C.S.	1987	Round Oval

P

PATERSON	L.M.	G.B.	1986	Long Oval
PERTHSHIRE EARLY	S.E.	G.B.	1963	Oval
PILGRIM	E.M.|	G.B.	1988	Long Oval
PIMPERNEL	E.M.	N.L.	1953	Oval
PINK DUKE OF YORK	F.E.	G.B.	1956	Long Oval
PINK FIR APPLE	L.M.	F.	1850	Long
POLLOCK'S PINK	F.E.	G.B.	1968	Round Oval
PRIZETAKER	S.E.|	G.B.	1882	Long Oval

R

RAEBURN'S G. CUPS	E.M.	G.B.	1924	Round
RANFURLY RED	E.M.	G.B.	1920	Round
READING RUSSET	S.E.	G.B.	1882	Round
RED ASHLEAF	F.E.	G.B.	1912	Long Oval
RED CARA	L.M.	I.R.L.	1976	Round Oval
RED CRAIGS ROYAL	S.E.	G.B.	1957	Long Oval
RED DRAYTON	E.M.	G.B.	1987	Round Oval
RED KIDNEY	M.	G.B.	1918	Long Oval
RED KING EDWARD	E.M.	G.B.	1916	Oval
RED LETTER	E.M.	G.B.	1934	Long Oval
RED PENTLAND BEAUTY	F.E.	G.B.	1962	Oval
RED PENTLAND LUSTRE	F.E.	G.B.	1975	Long Oval
RED PONTIAC	E.M.	U.S.A.	1954	Round
RED SALAD (POTATO)	E.M.	G.B.	1958	Oval
RED SKIN	E.M.	G.B.	1934	Round
RED STORMONT480	E.M.	G.B.	1966	Oval
RED ULSTER PREMIER	F.E.	G.B.	1961	Long Oval
RODE EERSTELING	F.E.	N.L.	1942	Long Oval
RODE PIPO	E.M.	N.L.	1982	Long Oval
ROMANO	E.M.	N.L.	1978	Round Oval
ROSAMUNDA	E.M.	S.	1974	Round Oval
ROSEVAL	E.M.	F.	1950	Long Oval
RUBINIA	F.E.	N.L.	1983	Long Oval

S

Variety	Maturity	Country	Year	Shape
SANGRIA	E.M.	N.L.	1993	Round Oval
SHAMROCK	L.M.	G.B.	1890	Round
SHARPE'S PINK SEEDLING	E.M.	G.B.	1891	Round
SKIRZA	S.E.	G.B.	1986	Long Oval
ST. AIDAN	E.M.	G.B.	1945	Oval
STEMSTER	E.M.	G.B.	1986	Long Oval
STROMA	S.E.	G.B.	1989	Long Oval

T

Variety	Maturity	Country	Year	Shape
THE TOWSE	F.E.	G.B.	1916	Round
TOSCA	L.M.	G.B.	1987	Oval
TRISTAR	E.M.	G.B.	1993	Round Oval

U

Variety	Maturity	Country	Year	Shape
ULSTER SOVEREIGN	E.M.	G.B.	1962	Oval
ULTIMUS	E.M.	N.L.	1935	Long Oval
UTILITY	E.M.	G.B.	1921	Round

V

Variety	Maturity	Country	Year	Shape
VAKON	E.M.	N.L.	1986	Round
VANESSA	F.E.	N.L.	1973	Long Oval

W

Variety	Maturity	Country	Year	Shape
WAVERLEY	E.M.	G.B.	1920	Long Oval
WOUDSTER	E.M.	N.L.	1960	Round Oval

Y

Variety	Maturity	Country	Year	Shape
YAM	L.M.	G.B.	1836	Round

BLUE SKINNED VARIETIES

Variety	Maturity	Country	Year	Shape

A

Variety	Maturity	Country	Year	Shape
ARRAN VICTORY	L.M.	G.B.	1918	Round Oval

B

Variety	Maturity	Country	Year	Shape
BLACK KIDNEY	S.E.	G.B.	1923	Long Oval
BLUE CATRIONA	S.E.	G.B.	1979	Long Oval
BLUE POTATO	L.M.	G.B.	1951	Round
BUTE BLUES	E.M.	G.B.	1923	Long Oval

C

Variety	Maturity	Country	Year	Shape
CONGO	L.M.	G.B.	1918	Long

E

EDGECOTE PURPLE	E.M.	G.B.	1916	Long Oval
EDZELL BLUE	S.E.	G.B.	1915|	Round

G

GARDEN FAVOURITE	S.E.	G.B.	1911	Kidney
GARDEN FILLER	F.E.	I.R.L.	1924	Long Oval

H

HARLEQUIN	S.E.	G.B.	1883	Round
HEATHER	S.E.	G.B.	1993	Long Oval
HERD LADDIE	S.E.	G.B.	1908	Round Oval
HIBERNIAN	S.E.	I.R.L.	1918	Long Oval

K

KEPPLESTONE KIDNEY	E.M.	G.B.	1919	Long Oval

L

LEWIS BLACK POTATO	E.M.	G.B.	1910	Round

M

MAUVE QUEEN	E.M.	G.B.	1915	Round
MORVEN	E.M.	G.B.	1988	Round Oval

P

PEERLESS	L.M.	G.B.	1918	Round
PRIDE OF BUTE	E.M.	G.B.	1918	Long

R

READING RUBY	S.E.	G.B.	1883	Kidney
RYECROFT PURPLE	L.M.	G.B.	1920	Round Oval

S

SHETLAND	S.E.	G.B.	1922	Round Oval
SKERRY BLUE	L.M.	G.B.	1846	Round Oval

T

THOMES	E.M.	I.R.L.	1924	Long Oval

PART BLUE SKINNED VARIETIES

Variety	Maturity	Country	Year	Shape
A				
ANGUS BEAUTY	L.M.	G.B.	1954	Long Oval
B				
BUCHAN BEAUTY	L.M..	G.B.	1922	Round
C				
CATRIONA	S.E.	G.B.	1920	Long Oval
COCO	S.E.	G.B.	1990	Long Oval
D				
DR. VERNON	F.E.	G.B.	1922	Long Oval
F				
FORTYFOLD	E.M.	G.B.	1836	Round
K				
KESTREL	S.E.	G.B.	1992	Long Oval
N				
NELKA	E.M.	N.L.	1988	Long Oval
NORTHERN B	E.M.	G.B.	1893	Long Oval
O				
OLD BLACK	L.M.	G.B.	1951	Round Oval

CODES USED IN POTATO LIST

COUNTRIES OF ORIGIN

A	AUSTRIA
AUS	AUSTRALIA
CDN	CANADA
CS	CZECHOSLOVAKIA
D	WEST GERMANY
DDR	EAST GERMANY
DK	DENMARK
F	FRANCE
GB	GREAT BRITAIN
IRL	IRELAND
N	NORWAY
NL	NETHERLANDS
NZL	NEW ZEALAND
S	SWEDEN
USA	UNITED STATES OF AMERICA

CODES FOR MATURITY

F.E.	First Early
S.E.	Second Early
E.M.	Early Maincrop
L.M.	Late Maincrop
M.	Maincrop